forever lounge

A LAID-BACK PRICE GUIDE TO THE LANGUID SOUNDS OF LOUNGE MUSIC

BY JOHN WOOLEY, THOMAS CONNER & MARK BROWN

ANTIQUE TRADER BOOKS
A DIVISION OF LANDMARK SPECIALTY BOOKS
NORFOLK, VIRGINIA

ISBN: 1-58221-004-7
Library of Congress Catalog Card Number: 98-88182

Editor: Tony Lillis
Photographer: Mike Keller
Price Consultant: Gary Johnson of Rockaway Records
Mentor: John Koenig
Designer: Mark Brown
Cover Design: Chris Decker

To order additional copies of this book, or to obtain a catalog, please contact:

Antique Trader Books
P.O. Box 1050
Dubuque, Iowa 52004
1-800-334-7165
www.collect.com

authors' dedication

For everyone who ever sat in my home and watched the flickering filmed images of old TV shows play elegantly across the living-room wall. For Jonathan and Steven, kids not only cool enough to watch black-and-white, but hip enough to dig it. And especially for Janis, for not being too jealous of Edie Hart. John Wooley

For my folks, who kept their Arthur Lyman records. For my compadres here, who proved that nine-to-five can be its own kind of cocktail hour. For Daniel, who surrenderred the Mac on demand and kept his beautiful, brave face when I attempted mint juleps. Thomas Conner

For Kelly, an A-1 kit-kat who brings the lounge to life. And to Bret, the smoothest, shakin'est top-dog of all. Mark Brown

'Who'd have thought that out of a genre as debased as 'easy listening' would come something so mind-curdling-ly bizarre and beautiful?'

Matt Groening
[creator of 'The Simpsons']

contents

Kelly Kurt

introduction

Listen for it and you'll hear it everywhere …

Weaving through the public discourse like cigarette smoke trailing past the shapes and faces in a crowded bar. The word is lounge, and not long ago, it was mostly just a vague pejorative. ("She used to really rock out, but now she's in some lounge band doing 'Moondance' three times a night.") These days, however, the word represents a rich and satisfying variety of images, from the suddenly re-hip Rat Pack's boozy camaraderie on and off Vegas stages to Esquivel's otherworldly big-band reworkings, from the lushly romantic sweep of a Jackie Gleason LP to the cool tough blast of a TV detective-show theme, circa 1960. Even much of the "easy listening" music cited by Mr. Groening, to many ears and psyches, settles neatly into the same category. We've even seen records by such far-flung acts as country's Glen Campbell and rock's Devo (!) gathered up under the "lounge" heading.

So what is it, and how did it come to be? To answer the second part of the question, you have to nail down the first – and no one, to our knowledge, has ever done a definitive job of that. Here, however, we'd like to take our shot, arrived at after endless discussions and debates – we know you've had them, too – about what constitutes this slippery label called "lounge." We boiled down our criteria to a few clear determinants, and these guided our choices of what to include in this guide and what to leave to the closet Carpenters fans to find on their own.

We decided that it's a lounge record if it:

… lures you into the 100-yard stare of fond memories – not gushy nostalgia, but the moment of life-reaffirming pause brought on by the music (no photograph captures this better than that of the woman on the cover of the ultimate lounge album, Jackie Gleason's *Music, Martinis and Memories*).

… in any way links its music to "cocktail time" or "the cocktail hour."

… concerns itself more with the listener's experience than that of the player(s).

… overtly or implicitly suggests – through titles or artwork – that playing the record will produce the same effects for your evening's companion as a dose of Spanish Fly in her drink.

… is overly concerned with exploring and presenting what in the '50s and '60s were new sounds – whether it's new stereo technology, such as Esquivel's "120 System," or new feats in instrumentation, like Dick Schory's use of more than 100 percussion instruments on one album.

… walks that hairline between bouncy camp and graceful dignity.

… features music evoking foreign oddities or exotic hedonism that wouldn't have crossed the funk threshold of most Eisenhower-Era Americans.

… sounds better as the ice bucket empties.

Finally, whether "exotica," cool jazz, stereo-enhanced percussion, or the more romantic forms of easy-listening, the whole notion of lounge music is finally, ultimately, subjective. All of it, even the new stuff being created by new bands, is really about the past – real or revisionist, but always idealized.

If you wonder whether a record is truly "lounge" or not, simply ask yourself what it evokes in you. If the answer is romance and twilight, liquor and languor, it's lounge. If it's your old aunt's antimacassared chair, it's not. Lounge is about chilled gin on your tongue, the scent of perfume in your nostrils, the promise of adventure in your head, and the enticing look of unfeigned interest, maybe even nascent love, in the eyes that meet yours across the table, over the frosted rim of a chilled glass.

It could be that the old phrase "mood music" describes the lounge sound as well as anything. The mood created by lounge music is like a powerful cocktail – several parts romance combined with a dash of satisfaction, a jigger of memory, and just a drop of danger – but it's a mood, nonetheless, very similar to those that were suddenly able to be created once the LP was born.

How It All Started

Mood music, of course, is as old as music itself. But recorded mood music really got jump-started in 1948. That was the year that Columbia released the first commercial 33 1/3 rpm long-playing discs. (According to music writer-historian Steve Ramm, "Columbia invited their chief rival RCA to join them in using that speed, but RCA wasn't sure. So in 1949 RCA introduced the 7-inch 45 rpm EP record, which finally died in the early 1970s.")

With the LP, or Long Player, listeners didn't have to jump up and turn a record over after every song, or stack a bunch of platters on the changer in order to hear more than one tune in a row. Now, there was time for a mood to curl up out of the grooves of a single disc, fifteen or twenty minutes that a person could relax, sip a drink, and be transported by the music. The innovative Columbia Records was quick to catch on to the mood possibilities – Paul Weston, the label's west coast musical director, came through early and often with titles like *Music For The Fireside*, *Music for A Rainy Night*, *Dream Time Music*, and even one called, simply, *Mood Music*.

Columbia also had the prolific Percy Faith, who began his long string of mood albums in the early '50s with such offerings as *Continental Music*, *Romantic Music*, and *Music Until Midnight*.

These orchestral records were in many ways the next step in the evolution of the big dance bands of the '30s and '40s. After WW II, as the big-band era died away, the vocalists – rather than the bandleaders – took over on the pop charts, signaling a trend away from the "name" orchestras and toward the singers who'd once worked for those bands but now had the name value to carry a record on their own. Meanwhile, big bands, as well as pop-tilted symphonic orchestras like those led by Mantovani, found refuge in the LPs, where they created volumes of instrumental music for the part of the audience that still wanted more than just radio hits.

With the late '50s, the bachelor-pad lifestyle came into existence as a pop-culture phenomenon, lived by literate, mostly college-educated males who dug cool jazz and beatnik poetry, read the men's magazines of the day, knew the names of exotic alcoholic drinks and what went into them, and understood the Playboy philosophy, then being given its first big test-drive by bachelor-pad guru Hugh Hefner. They were refined and urbane, able to discuss Schopenhauer and Ingmar Bergman with equal facility. They were also as horny as wild goats, but practiced at not letting their lust bubble through in public. It was cool to be hip, and hip to be cool, and a whole subgenre of music came along to provide a soundtrack for the times. Sometimes lush, sometimes lightly swinging, it was always a good background for seduction, whether real or imagined, as well as for the 3 a.m. drink that went down as lonely as a Chet Baker riff. These guys knew about and appreciated rock 'n' roll, but their association with it always seemed sort of academic, as if they were just a little above that whole teenage thing.

At about the same time, late '50s and early '60s, Vegas was happening, and happening not only as an entertainment mecca, but as a lifestyle. Here, Sinatra and Dino and Sammy and the rest drank and smoked and chased women through endless neon nights, occasionally stopping to do shows that reflected their off-stage shenanigans – art imitating life. These were the true "lounge" musicians, singing and joking and cavorting their way through the lounges of Sin City, drink in one hand, smoldering cigarette in the other, never mussing their hair, never wrinkling their suits.

The bachelor-pad mentality and the Vegas lounge lifestyle were both important components of lounge music. But maybe the biggest influence of all, at least as far as middle America was concerned, came along on September 22nd of 1958. That's when NBC-TV beamed the first episode of a series called *Peter Gunn* into millions of unsuspecting homes, ushering in a network-television detective-show craze and giving us two of lounge music's biggest icons: Peter Gunn and Edie Hart.

Gunn, as played by the impossibly suave Craig Stevens, could've been a bachelor-pad poster boy, with an added fillip of two-fisted toughness. Edie, as played by the wonderfully sensual Lola Albright, was not only his girlfriend, but a whispery jazz singer in a club called Mother's, where Gunn spent a lot of his time. The music was by a young West Coast hep cat by the name of Mancini. It was very good, and there was plenty of it – much more than just the show's theme, now such a part of American pop-music legend that high-school bands play it between the halves of football games on bucolic fields all across America.

Peter Gunn, said writer and TV-theme expert Jon Burlingame in a recent newspaper interview, was "the first television series where music took on an importance all its own." And because the series ran for three years, untold millions of people young and old visited Mother's for a dose of music – far more people than ever sat foot in a real jazz or Vegas lounge. The influence of Mancini and Peter Gunn – as well as the other cool-p.i. TV series – on lounge music's popularity is simply incalculable.

Finally, there's the "space-age" thing to consider. In the late '50s, when Russia launched a sneak attack on space with Sputnik, setting America to wondering how quickly we could get a satellite up

into that inky void, and if the Russkies could actually beat us to the moon, a couple of things happened. First, the romance of science was reawakened in the populace, and pop-culture began showing a preoccupation with what might be Out There. Second, technology suddenly took on new importance, as American scientists worked to win what was then termed the race for space.

No surprise, then, that otherworldly sounds – whether made electronically or by the human voice – began showing up on instrumental records. And not only that, but sometimes the backs of albums began looking like technical manuals, with windy small-print tech-head explanations of high-fidelity and, later, stereo techniques used in recording. Sometimes, as in the previously cited "120 System" used on some of Esquivel's space-age pop albums, you got both these components in one package.

The 'Easy Listening' Problem

You could say, with some justification, that classic lounge music croaked sometime in the early '60s, done in at least partially by the Beatles and the subsequent transmogrification of rock 'n' roll into a hip and happenin' thing called 'rock,' a musical form adults could not only groove on with impunity but also discuss with all sorts of cannibas-fueled college-level *gravitas*. But the music and the people who made it didn't suddenly just disappear. For instance, one of lounge's real pioneers, the conductor-arranger Don Ralke (*But You've Never Heard Gershwin With Bongos*) was a prime mover in the creation of the 1966 album *One Stormy Night*, by The Mystic Moods, as was a recording engineer and producer named Brad Miller. "Brad Miller was fooling around with sound effects, and he took a Jackie Gleason album and put thunder and lightning and stuff behind it, and gave a tape to a San Francisco deejay," Ralke recalled in a 1997 conversation. "He played it over the air and the switchboard lit up. So Brad Miller came to me, told me what had happened, and he said, 'I'd like to have some product, but I don't have any money.' I happened to have some cuts in my closet that we put together. He had one or two cuts. He put a train sound in, and it immediately took off."

The Mystic Moods albums, which were requirement in every college dorm room and frat house for many years, pioneered the idea of environmental sounds wedded to romantic orchestral music. They may have been more influential than they've been given credit for, too. It's not completely outrageous to link *One Stormy Night* with the Beach Boys' classic *Pet Sounds*, for instance – listen to the train noises and lonely barking dogs on the latter's "Caroline, No," as well as the album's pair of full-orchestra instrumentals. Certainly, *One Stormy Night* and the rest of the Mystic Moods' discs showed that there was still a market out there for instrumental mood music.

The Mystic Moods are only one example of the musical style that came to be known as easy-listening, or elevator, music. That's the category in which a lot of people put the string versions of rock hits, the quasi-classical romantic music, the acts that defy facile categorization, like Ferrante & Teicher or the Tijuana Brass. We believe, however, that although the difference between a true easy-listening disc and an LP that belongs in this book is one of degrees, the distinction needs to be made. Elevator music is just that – music to timid to step out of the background, of a completely non-confrontational and plain vanilla nature, music meant to soothe without registering on any conscious level – like the plain girl who serves punch at the senior prom. It fulfills some sort of minor function efficiently enough, but you don't really remember it.

Does something like Ray Martin's baroque version of "Georgia on My Mind" belong there? How about the Hollyridge Strings' instrumental take on "Yesterday's Gone," or "Trains and Boats and Planes" by Chet Baker and the Carmel Strings? Sure, it's all in the ear of the beholder, and one listener's delight will be another's aural wallpaper. But when in doubt as to whether it belonged in this book, we applied our own criteria (the ones we listed a couple of pages back); if the record seemed to fit, it was in like Flynn, holding its head up next to Esquivel, Martin Denny, Mancini, and all the rest of the big guys.

Even with that, and even though we know we've found and cataloged most LPs that might fit with our definition of lounge, we know we haven't rounded up every lounge disc ever cut. Maybe we've even missed one of your favorites. After all, *Forever Lounge* was begun with a deep interest, not a database. It was our desire to explore and learn and offer up our findings about lounge discs that brought this book to life. We've done hundreds of hours of research in libraries, record collections, and on the Internet. We've spent hundreds more hours listening and compiling and writing and listening some more.

But even with the thousands of entries we've come up with, we realize that *Forever Lounge*, like any other price guide, is a work in progress. We know that there are people out there who know more than we do about this – or, at least, about certain aspects of this – and who probably know of LPs that need to be in these pages.

We invite those people to write us, letting us know what sin of omission – or even commission – they believe we've committed here; we'll gratefully take it under advisement for the next edition of *Forever Lounge*. Those who don't tell us otherwise will also get an acknowledgement if we use their suggestions. You can reach us c/o John Wooley, Box 133, Foyil, OK 74031 or via the Internet at loungemuse@aol.com. We respectfully request that no letter begin with "I can't believe you morons left out …" or variations on that theme. Lounge, above all else, is cool, and so are restraint and civility.

Finally, our most fervent wish is that you catch the spirit we hope permeates these pages, a spirit that gently takes the edges of life and disguises them, at least for awhile, with a glow as cold and beautiful as a firefly's light. To paraphrase the back of that famous Jackie Gleason album: You can do it with music, with memories, with martinis.

So mix your own martinis, or order one up from your favorite bartender. We've got your music and memories right here.

John Wooley, Thomas Conner and Mark Brown
August 1998

**Pete and
Edie**

*The lovely Lola
Albright and the
ultrasuave Craig
Stevens.*

how to use this guide

Our common impulse in creating *Forever Lounge* was the impulse that fuels a lot of writers: to celebrate and further explore something that intrigues and amuses us mightily and to communicate our findings to other interested people. In this case, what captivates us is that amoeba-like musical category called lounge; we want this book to be of use to people, like ourselves, who love the stuff, would like to know more about it, and, yes, may even be thinking about picking up a few simoleons with it somewhere along the line – or, at the very least, may need to have an idea of whether or not that copy of *Leis of Jazz* spotted on a record-convention table is really worth its $20 sticker price.

We'll give the clichéd answer first, which is, if it's worth it to you, then it's worth it. But for those who want a little more guidance, pricewise,

we've enlisted the help of Rockaway Records' Gary Johnson to advise us. We're collectors of and listeners to lounge music, and we cheerfully admit that we deferred entirely to Gary, a universally acknowledged vinyl expert who meticulously gave us his estimated prices on the thousands of discs listed herein. There would be no price guide without him, and there would probably be no *Forever Lounge* in any form if not for the godfatherly advice and help of John Koenig, wonderful editor of the equally swell record-collectors' magazine Discoveries. Without these two first-raters, their reputations as well as their tireless help, we not only would have no book; we also would have no credibility.

With that in mind, then, here's how to use our price guide.

How We Organized the Discographies

First of all, our albums are listed under artist, with a separate listing for various-artist compilations. After the "artist" listing, the discs are arranged alphabetically by label, and then in chronological order under each label, with titles followed by LP number (two numbers usually refer to mono and stereo editions; we've tried to note reissues) and year of release, if we know it. The marginal comments, which tend to focus on the more obscure artists and discs, are an attempt to keep things lively by giving the browser something other than lists, prices, and pictures.

Forever Lounge lists discographies of 12-inch and 10-inch LPs. Lounge artists scored hit singles, too, but we have avoided the intricate listing of singles and 78 rpms – both worth entire volumes on their own. Plus, we're trying to wrangle the ethos of "lounge," which isn't as flighty and fickle as the more single-driven pop side of the industry. Ever tried to concentrate on a cocktail or woo women while spinning 45s? Lounge music became lounge music because the LP – long player – allowed lush lads to set the record playing and have a good half hour to concentrate on … more important things.

Also, in our attempt to keep the focus on lounge and cocktail mood music, we have not always listed every album by every artist. These are not meant to be complete artist discographies. For instance, Herb Alpert made some great lounge records with and without the Tijuana Brass, but his career is hardly defined by the orthophonic oeuvre. Even Sinatra and Dean Martin made records that don't really qualify as lounge. Therefore, we trimmed their discographies to include only those albums that fit a concept of lounge music we hope is universal.

The listings include only U.S. releases unless a foreign edition is somehow relevant, well-known or readily available. Many CD reissues are included by such foreign labels as Bear Family (Germany), Bainbridge (UK) or Varese Sarabande.

Finally, because we are fans first and collectors second, we've included in our listings notations that tell you if an album or artist is also available on compact disc. As CD technology has gotten more affordable, labels large and microscopic have rushed in to reissue a dizzying variety of music, including lots of lounge. If you're just wanting to listen to the stuff, this is a great place to start. (We also acknowledge the fact that there'll be even more lounge CDs on the market by the time *Forever Lounge* sees print, given the breakneck pace of the reissue biz. We've tried to stay current right up to deadline with our listings.)

How to Read the Price Quotes

Whether it's a price guide on Prussian bayonets, Big Little Books, or eight-track tapes, the caveat is always the same when it comes to pricing guidelines: READ THIS SECTION BEFORE BUYING OR SELLING. They put it in World War III typeface and people still ignore it, choosing instead to look up a particular item in their possession and fix immediately on the highest price listed. This is human nature of some sort. This is also a mistake.

Here's the deal: Unless you've got something in truly, genuinely, near mint condition – which we'll describe exactly in a moment – what you've got is worth far less than the top-end price. It really is that simple.

Forever Lounge gives you two price levels. The high one is for near mint, which few records are. The low one is for very good-plus condition, a far more likely, but still desirable, condition.

Why these two, and not any lower ones? According to John Koenig, "It's very basic. Most dealers don't stock records in good condition. There's no demand. And the only time anyone

grades a record 'fair' is when it's an impossibly rare record, so just having it is more important than condition. Robert Johnson 78s, Hank Williams on the Sterling label – it doesn't matter whether tractors drove over records like those."

The esteemed Mr. Koenig is talking about rural blues and country there, of course; it's far more likely that a disc in this book was taken from near mint to fair by an unfortunate accident involving sloe gin or an elbow on the tone arm than by anything related to farm equipment. But whatever the reason, any album in less than very good (VG) condition can be picked up for far less, which is good news for listeners, bad news for people who want to sell things for more than they're worth.

Again, please, never automatically take the top price. In fact, those who're in the record-selling business succeed by not only realistically grading and pricing their stuff, but by knocking off an extra buck or two as well. As Doug Hanners, longtime guru of the Austin Record Convention, puts it: "More and more people who are new to the business are coming in, and they tend to take the price guides literally … They see the money being made, and they may have an interest in or a fondness for music, but they don't have enough knowledge of the business to know how it works at a record show. Grading is a problem, too, when they don't grade correctly.

"Usually, though, they figure out they're not going to get those prices, and then they either quit, or they drop their prices. If they do that, drop their prices, then they'll make money at these shows."

Grade correctly, drop prices. It's a simple formula. We can't advise nascent dealers on how much to knock off, but we can tell dealers and other aficionados exactly what the grades are, thanks to John Koenig and Discoveries:

Near Mint: This record may show very slight signs of wear and use, but will have no audible defect. Sleeves and labels in this condition may show marginal deterioration that will keep them from being graded mint (which is, basically, original, unsealed condition), but will not have any repairs or marks from pen or pencil. RECORDS IN THIS CONDITION ARE WORTH THE FIRST AMOUNT IN THE PRICE GUIDE.

VERY GOOD: Records will be noticeably less than perfect. They obviously have been played, but the damage is not visually or audibly distracting. Minor scuffs and slight surface defects may be present. Background ticks and hiss are minimal. Sleeves may show some slight ring wear [wear in the shape of the record or label inside] and may have minor creases. Seams will be intact unless they have separated due to failure of manufacturer's gluing agent. RECORDS IN VERY GOOD-PLUS CONDITION ARE WORTH THE SECOND AMOUNT IN THE PRICE GUIDE.

PLEASE NOTE: THE PRICES ARE FOR STEREO ALBUMS. IF STEREO VERSIONS OF THE ALBUMS DON'T EXIST, THEN THE PRICES ARE FOR MONO. IF STEREO VERSIONS DO EXIST, KNOCK 75% OFF FOR A MONO VERSION.

As you can see, there's a lot of turf between NM and VG, and you'll often find dealers using the category "excellent" or other terms to describe a record that's somewhere between these two conditions. We've used VG+ to determine our second tier of prices.

Like the records themselves, collectors are found at all sorts of levels. Some try to acquire nothing but near-mint, or even mint, records; others are just as happy with something they can play for themselves, their pals, and their parties, either by slipping the original vinyl onto a turntable or by taping it for future use. The latter category of aficionados will likely be happy with something in less than VG shape, especially since a lot of LP surface noise can be ameliorated with present-day equipment. (Okay, we know a turntable doesn't exactly constitute "present-day equipment," but you know what we mean.) For the less-discriminating lounge-music fan – and we put ourselves in that category – there are these lower (or "bargain") grades:

GOOD: (worth about 30% of VG price) This

record will have both visual and audible distractions, but will still be playable. The record and sleeve will show visual wear and moderate use. Sleeves will show ring wear, but will not be physically damaged.

FAIR: (worth about 10% of VG price) This record is visually and audibly distracting. It will still play although obviously damaged and will not have skips, but may have "play through" scratches. It is still usable. Sleeves will show heavy ring wear and some minor physical damage.

There is one step below "fair," a sad and brutal drop into the oblivion of the unwanted. Discoveries calls this fatal state "poor"; we've always called it "sidewalked." It's a record with a beat-up sleeve and a record inside that'll be hard to listen to, assuming it plays at all. LPs of this condition are mostly of value to owners of retro bars who want something to hammer onto their walls, or to skeet shooters looking for a cheap alternative to clay pigeons.

If you dig around flea markets and record conventions for any length of time, you'll find a few of these sad specimens – slipped into a sparkling new polyethylene sleeve and marked with a mint-level price.

Don't buy them.

Instead, armed with the knowledge in this book, buy decent records at a decent price. And keep in mind that even with all the record price guides that've been on the market for years, you've still got a good chance of picking up a good-plus condition Three Suns or Martin Denny disc for less than a buck at some thrift shop or Salvation Army bookstore, as well as at a record convention or used-disc store.

So that's how to use this book. But there's one more thing we feel compelled to say: This is a guide, not a bible. We hope that it guides you safely and surely into the soothingly exotic musical stream of lounge, and that you'll let the current carry you away. That's what the music does, and that's what it's all about.

prices

Note

The two prices listed after each disc are, in order, for records in Near Mint (NM) and Very Good-Plus (VG+) condition.
See the "How To Use This Guide" section for more information.

The prices indicated are for stereo versions of the album, if they exist, mono otherwise.
A mono version of an album also released in stereo is worth 25% of the stereo disc.

All prices listed are U.S. dollar amounts.

There may be a more intriguing album pairing than that of Herb Jeffries and Eden Ahbez on *The Singing Prophet*, but if there is, we don't know it. Ahbaz was a song-writer-mystic, best-known for writing Nat King Cole's big hit "Nature Boy," who lived like an Old Testament prophet in the Hollywood Hills. Jeffries (born Herbert Jeffrey) was the screen's first black singing cowboy (starring in four indie westerns in the 1930s as "Bob Blake"), a member of the big bands of Earl "Fatha" Hines and Duke Ellington (he was the vocalist on Ellington's million-selling single "Flamingo"), a Parisian nightclub owner, and the star of the 1957 Allied Artists musical *Calypso Joe*.

At this writing, Jeffries was deep in his eighties and still active in the business, a true American-music treasure recording for the Warner Western label. Ahbaz lasted almost as long. He was 86 in 1995, when he died of head injuries sustained in a wreck near Desert Hot Springs, Ca.

Note: In all his years of dealing records, Gary Johnson has never seen this album. – JW

Leo **Addeo**

Addeo's More Hawaii in Hi-Fi *features a great version of Anton Karas's "Third Man Theme," simply dripping with Pacific sea water!*
– TC

Even the Hawaiians Buy Addeo's Music!
[blurb on the back of *Songs of Hawaii*]

Larry **Adler**

On CD: Meastro of the Mouth Organ (ASV, 1995); Rhapsody in Blue (Avid, 1995); Mouth Organ Virtuoso (EMI, 1995); The Great Larry Adler Plays Standards on Harmonica (Pearl, 1996)

Eden **Ahbez**

"In the summer of 1960, Ahbez returned to the material world long enough to record "Eden's Island," a 12-song meditation on isolation, nature and free love for Bob Keane's Del-Fi Records. An alternately soothing and unsettling mixture of Martin Denny-ish exotica and sub-Beat poetry, "Eden's Island" features the liquid pianoscapes of Stan Kenton sideman Paul Moer, Ahbez's ethereal wooden flute, a chorus of "island girls," and as many different sea, wind, and tropical bird sound effects as the Keane's production team could muster. One track, "The Old Boat," features the incredible sound effect of a creaking wood boat, and "Surf Rider," (not the same song as the Lively Ones' classic surf rumbler) also features "Eden's" bouyant pop vocals.

"Martin Denny was real big at the time" recalls Keane. "He had all that shit ... parrots in the background, and the birds and the tropical stuff, so I felt 'Eden's Island' would be a great album, because it was along those lines. It was a suite to him. You kind of get the feeling like maybe he wanted to be a philosopher or something, but actually his lyrics were not philosophical. He was trying to paint pictures with his music, I think, which he did very well."

[from Ahbez's bio on the Del-Fi web site]

On CD: Echoes From Nature Boy (Accent, 1995); Eden's Island (Del-Fi, 1996)

Manny **Albam**

Perhaps *Eddie Albert and Margo* – featuring the man who'd later gain his biggest fame as the back-to-nature Manhattanite on televison's *Green Acres* and his wife, the actress, dancer and castinet player remembered as the star of the 1943 cult classic *The Leopard Man* – takes a bit of stretching to pull into the lounge camp. Certainly, the material ("September Song," "Hello Young Lovers," "Jenny Kissed Me") is here, and all the theatrical narratives, not to mention Margo's castanets on one track, create a certain offbeat sense of romance. Besides, it's the only album ever recorded to feature a reading of John Maesfield's classic poem "Sea Fever" over a lush orchestral version of "Ebb Tide."

– JW

Of course, Julie London was and forever will be the queen of bachelor-pad. But let's

take a moment here to acknowledge the lovely Ms. Lola Albright, whose recorded

output was far less prodigious than that of Ms. London, but who made up for it by

appearing in millions of homes once a week from 1958 through '60, whispering

throaty vocals through the smoky haze of an archetypal, pretend lounge called

Mother's and smiling only when her main dude, the ultra-cool p.i. Peter Gunn,

showed up for a quick one.

Craig Stevens, the star of the fondly remembered TV show, has said that *Peter

Gunn* was the first series in which viewers knew that a man and woman, not hus-

band and wife, were sleeping with each other. Certainly, there was a sexy aura

about Ms. Albright's black-and-white vocal turns that time has done nothing to

diminish. It's the same quality that's captured on *Dreamsville*, with music by *Peter

Gunn*'s Mancini, a swinging, evocative LP that belongs in the forefront of any

lounge-music collection.

– JW

Lola's lounge

*Lola Albright
in action.*

Guitarist Laurindo Almeida was one of the seminal figures in the bossa nova craze that swept across America in the '60s. Landing on Capitol Records after leaving his native Brazil, Almeida assembled a group of jazz musicians and proceeded to show the world that any song could be given that lightly swinging, percussion – and acoustic-guitar based bossa nova treatment. Among the more unlikely candidates Almeida bossa-novaed on his Capitol LPs were "Hava Nagila," the hard-boiled theme from TV's *Naked City*, and Dick Dale's surf classic "Misirlou."

– JW

Eddie **Albert** and Margo

Lola **Albright**

"Welcome to Dreamsville, a contemporary Nepenthe discovered and populated by Lola Albright, actress, singer and visual delight. Together with the orchestra under the direction of Hank Mancini, Miss Albright sketches in the topography of a dozen superior songs, wafting the listener along with soft and insinuating tones to a particularly pleasurable state of mind …"
  [from the liner notes for *Dreamsville*]

Ronnie **Aldrich** and
His Two Pianos

On CD: Silver Bells (Essex, 1992); Great Themes to Remember (PolyGram Special Markets, 1995); Twin Piano Magic (Rebound, 1995); Christmas With Ronnie Aldrich (PolyGram Special Markets, 1996)

Van **Alexander**

Steve **Allen**

In addition to winning over international audiences with his own material, Steve Allen's hi-fi-falutin' ivory tinkling worked with talent of all kinds. Steve Allen Plays the Piano Greats includes his readings of pieces by Claude Thornhill, Gordon Jenkins, Carmen Cavallero and Erroll Garner. His eponymous album finds him joined by Steve Lawrence, Eydie Gormé, Pat Kirby and Skitch Henderson.
  – TC

On CD: Plays Hi-Fi Music for Influentials (Varese Sarabande, 1996)

Laurindo **Almeida**

"A lot has been said about Herb Alpert's Tijuana Brass, and there's a lot more to be said about them. Their popularity has grown enormously in the two years since admirers started shouting "Ole!" for "The Lonely Bull."

"It began with the teenagers, we thought. But at the Brass' debut as concert artists in San Francisco, we noticed, to our delight, that it's easier to skin an amoeba than to catalog the 'Typical Tijuana Brass Fan.' The teens were there, but so were the 'hippies' and the 'squares,' the 'little old ladies' and the screen starlets, the celebrities and those who make them celebrities. In fact, one admirer, who looked as though he stepped from a page in Esquire said, 'You would think that a lot of these people would be home watching the man who serves the bubbles ...'"

[from the liner notes for *Whipped Cream and Other Delights*]

Trumpeter-songwriter Herb Alpert and his L.A. pal Lou Adler wrote "Wonderful World" for Sam Cooke and produced early Jan & Dean singles on the Dore label (including the 1959 hit "Baby Talk"). In '62, he got a new partner, West Coast promotion man Jerry Moss, and they formed the Carnival label, which became A&M (for Alpert and Moss). A&M's first big hit was 1962's "The Lonely Bull," an instrumental Alpert had cut earlier (under a different title), goosed up with authentic bullfight-crowd noises and reissued. It began a baker's dozen of Top 40 hits for Alpert's Tijuana Brass, concluding in 1967 with "A Banda (Ah Bahn-da)." All but 1966's "Mame," which featured limited vocals, were strictly instrumental.

Alpert's direct, economical, often overdubbed horn work, with the

On CD: *Brazilian Soul [with Charlie Byrd] (Concord Picante, 1987); Virtuoso Guitar (Laserlight, 1991); Artistry in Rhythm (Concord Jazz, 1994); Dance the Bossa Nova (Saludos Amigos, 1994); Best of Laurindo Almeida and the Bossa Nova All-Stars (Curb, 1996); Three Guitars Three (Pro Arte); Virtuso Guitar (LaserLight); La Four Scores (Concord Jazz); The Best of Laurindo Almeida (Curb)*

Herb **Alpert** and the Tiajuana Brass

On CD: Classics, Vol. 1 (A&M, 1987); Classics, Vol. 20 (A&M, 1987)

maracas and tambourines shaking along behind, became one of the most recognizable sounds of the '60s, inspiring imitators like World Pacific's Mariachi Brass with Chet Baker. Sometime too peppy to fit comfortably into the lounge category, the Brass' music nonetheless is evocative, often romantic, and – now that three decades have passed since its heyday – more than a little exotic-sounding as well.

– JW

Kip **Anderson**
and the Tides

Shango! Night in a Quiet Village .... 5 - 3
   (Kapp)

Leroy **Anderson**

Leroy Anderson Conducts .... 5 - 3
   (Decca DL-8121)
A Leroy Anderson "Pops" Concert .... 5 - 3
   (Decca DL-9749)

Maya **Angelou**

Miss Calypso .... 50 - 30

On CD: Miss Calypso (Scamp SCP-9705-2, 1996)

Miss **Ann-Margret**

The Vivacious One .... 25 - 15
   (RCA Victor LSP-2551, 1962)
And Here She Is .... 25 - 15
   (RCA Victor 1961)
Beauty and the Beard [with Al Hirt] .... 25 - 15
   (RCA Victor)

On CD: Many Moods of Ann-Margret (Raven [Australia], 1984); Let Me Entertain You [boxed set] (RCA, 1996)

Ray **Anthony**

Not only did Ray Anthony write the staid, solid theme for the TV cop show Dragnet, *but he also wrote a somehow timeless tune that's had people young and old shaking cottontails – the "Bunny Hop."*
– TC

Dancing in the Dark .... 5 - 3
   (Aerospace RA-995)
Dream Dancing Around the World .... 5 - 3
   (Aerospace RA-1007)
I've Never Been in Love Before .... 5 - 3
   (Blue Heaven BH5-503)

Antonio and His Italianos

Alfred **Apaka**

Mario Ruiz **Armengol**

Leo **Arnaud**

Chet **Atkins**

Hi Fi in Focus .... 25 - 15
   (RCA Victor LPM-1577, 1957)
Mister Guitar .... 25 - 15
   (RCA Victor LSP-2103, 1959)
The Other Chet Atkins .... 25 - 15
   (RCA Victor LSP-2175, 1960)
Plays the Great Movie Themes [double 7-inch EP] .... 25 - 15
   (RCA Victor LPC-124, 1961)
Caribbean Guitar .... 25 - 15
   (RCA Victor LSP-2549, 1962)
Travelin' Guitar [produced by Anita Kerr] .... 25 - 15
   (RCA Victor LPM-2678, 1963)

Jan **August**

Plays Songs to Remember .... 5 - 3
   (Mercury MG-20072)
Music for the Quiet Hour... 5 - 3
   (Mercury MG-20078)
Plays Great Piano Hits .... 5 - 3
   (Mercury MG-20513)
Accent! Latin Piano... 5 - 3
   (Mercury MG-20618/SR-60189)
Jan August Styles the Great Pop Piano Classics .... 5 - 3
   (Mercury MG-20659)
Piano Favorites by Jan August .... 5 - 3
   (Mercury MG-25087)
The Piano Wizardry of Jan August .... 5 - 3
   (Mercury MG-20276)

Georgie **Auld**

In The Land of Hi-Fi .... 5 - 3
   (EmArcy MG-36060, 1955)
Dancing in the Land of Hi-Fi .... 5 - 3
   (EmArcy MG-36090, 1956)
Sax Gone Latin .... 5 - 3
   (Capitol 1045, 1958)
Georgie Auld Plays for Melancholy Babies .... 5 - 3
   (Paramount 287, 1959)
Hawaii on the Rocks .... 5 - 3
   (Jaro JAS-8003, 1959)

Eugene Baird was a featured vocal-ist with Don McNeill's famous radio show *The Breakfast Club* and a singer with the bands of Tony Pastor and Paul Whiteman. On *Eugene Baird Sings – Duke's Boys Play Duke Ellington,* the Pittsburgh native appears with such famed Ellington "boys" as saxophonist Ben Webster, trombone-vibraphonist Tyree Glenn, and Duke's own son Mercer, who conducted and arranged the disc.

– JW

Bud **Averill**

Ethel **Azama**

Ethel Azama was a Japanese-Hawaiian singer with a small but mighty voice well-suited for the hair-pin turns of exotic melodies. Exotic Dreams is noted chiefly for its producer: Martin Denny.
  – TC

Burt **Bacharach**

On CD: Reach Out (A&M, 1995); Songbook (Alex, 1995); The Best of Burt Bacharach (A&M, 1996); The Look of Love: The Classic Songs of Burt … (Polygram, 1996); Plays the Burt Bacharach Hits (MCA, 1997); A Man & His Music (Spectrum, 1998)

Pearl **Bailey**

On CD: 16 Most Requested Songs (Columbia, 1991); Some of the Best (Delta 1996); More of the Best (Delta, 1996)

Eugenie Baird

Chet **Baker**

"The Baker horn … the Nietzsche pen … the talented musical support … Is this any way to run a record date? You bet it is!"

[from John Tynan's liner notes for *A Taste of Tequila*]

Sometimes disparagingly referred to as "Chet Baker's elevator music," the discs the legendary trumpeter-flugelhornist made with the Mariachi Brass and the Carmel Strings in the mid-'60s nonetheless have their own peculiar charm. The former outfit was a direct knockoff of Herb Alpert's Tijuana Brass, the latter one of those orchestras that specialized in instrumental versions of pop vocal hits, a la Andre Kostelanetz. Both were, of course, studio groups; arranger-conductors included the likes of George Tipton, Harry Betts and Jack "Lonely Surfer" Nitzsche.

Baker aficionados insist that these records were done at a time in the musician's troubled life when he would do about anything for money, and his parts certainly appear to be

[Continued on next page]

[Continued from previous page]

phoned in. It's not a stretch to imagine that he did all his work on every one of the albums in one afternoon. But there's a certain weird pleasure in hearing one of those wonderfully lonely Baker riffs dropped down in the middle of, say, an orchestral arrangement of "Got To Get You into My Life" or an ersatz-Tijuana Brass-style "Speedy Gonzales." No other musical experience is quite like it.

– JW

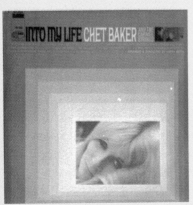

While Chet Baker was a bit too much of a straight-ahead jazzman to find his entire catalog included in this book, he certainly had his loungier moments. And never was he more the embodiment of lounge than when he sang.

Apparently, his tenor-range voice caused something of a stir in jazz circles. As John William Hardy wrote in the liner notes to *Chet Baker Sings*, "I remember when about half the present album came out in ten-inch form that the reactions to Baker's singing were varied indeed. A couple of critics including Nat Hentoff noted Chet's musical approach to phrasing and time that

are characteristic of instrumentalists who sing, and at least Hentoff liked the resulting album. But there were problems of acceptance, nevertheless. Although I have never understood why, there are many people – even jazz fans – who confuse and equate manliness with broad shoulders, baritone to bass voices, a generally barssy tone, (in demeanor and horn sound) and a kind of, well, pubic bulge about a human's physico-psychological makeup. People, especially jazz buffs should be hipper. The real ones are of course. The more troubling anit-Baker-sings individuals became downright angry at hearing him, and you can imagine what their troubles were. Girls who were unmoved (and thought Chet sounded like a girl) had eyes for football players (where I went to school) and wore falsies. At that time (1954-5) the same people thought pleatless trousers were funny, delicious, were better than winesap apples, and when you said cabernet sauvignon they said bourbon. Which is kind of a warped and uneven attitude."

Well, there'll be none of that here. Baker's vocalizing, like his trumpet playing, is both romantic and distant, warm and detached, like a three-martini-induced recollection of a long-ago love affair, in which the object of your affection stays always and forever young, desireable, and tucked into the shadows, just out of reach of your arms.

All that jazz

Lounge music laps over into so many other musical styles, from big-band and easy-listening to hard-core jazz, that the whole concept of its existence remains fluid and imperfect . It's especially hard to make a call with some of the famous jazz artists: Is, for instance, jazz legend Chet Baker – who is unmatched in his ability to create a hauntingly sad and lonely mood – a lounge-music act?

We think Chet's more straight jazz (although we've included a couple of the weirder permutations of his talent between these covers). Maybe the same could be said for Dave Brubeck, too. But we think Brubeck belongs here not only because his jazz is unfailingly accessible, but also because of his strong and creative ties to pop culture. "Take Five," of course, may be the best-known jazz number of all time, but albums like *Dave Digs Disney* (in which he and the boys re-interpret Disney movie tunes) and *Gone With the Wind* (an album of Southern-style tunes that include both Stephen Foster and "Georgia on My Mind") show that he bridges the gap between introspective jazzer and listener-oriented artist.

Plus, just about every track he ever recorded sounds great at 4 a.m. *John Wooley*

Fabulous Baker boy
Oklahoma native Chet Baker.

"*There's a paradox lurking somewhere in these grooves: Chet Baker is one of the most honest instrumentalists on the current scene, yet there are strings attached to this album. Ordinarily, the two concepts would cancel each other, but here the combination is musically gratifying …*"
[from the Burt Nelson liner notes for *Into My Life*]

Our favorite Chet Baker Story

Before falling to his death out of an Amsterdam hotel window in the late 1980s, Yale, Oklahoma's Chet Baker was one of jazz music's most storied practitioners, a profoundly troubled, drug-addicted soul who was nonetheless the epitome of cool – and sometimes, paradoxically, of innocence as well.

The great New Orleans trumpeter Al Hirt told us a story about Baker, working in Italy in the '50s.

One day, the manager of the club where Baker was playing asked him if Mussolini's son – who loved jazz and was a pretty fair keyboard player – could sit in that evening? Chet said sure, and before too long, Mussolini's son was brought in, with much ceremony, to meet the American jazzman. Introductions were made, the two shook hands, and Baker said, by way of conversation, "Sure was a drag about your dad."

– JW

ke *Peter Gunn* and *Johnny*

taccato, 77 Sunset Strip helped link

"lounge" and "cool" in the heads

f viewers all across America. The

our-long detective show featured

he jive-spouting character Kookie

layed by Ed Byrnes), who parked

ars at Dino's Lounge next door

hen he wasn't corralling scofflaws

ith p.i. pals Stu Bailey (Efrem

imbalist Jr.) and Jeff Spencer

Roger Smith). And Bailey and

pencer not only often met their

lients over a drink in the lounge,

ut occasionally took the stage to

o a little singing as well. The *77*

Sunset Strip album, with songs like

"Late at Bailey's Pad" and "Blue

Night on the Strip," is archetypal TV

azz, and first-rate lounge music.

– JW

Don **Baker**

Warren **Barker**

"Music is an integral part of '77 Sunset Strip,' and that it has contributed much to the outstand-ing success of the new Warner Bros.-ABC-TV show is axiomatic. The light touch of comedy, inter-esting characters and music which reflects the pulse of the glamorous Sunset Strip bind the show together each week. The excitement of this fabulous boulevard of bright lights and cozy hide-aways, where the good and the bad, the rich and the not-so-rich, but the always interesting live their drama filled lives, is part and parcel of '77 Sunset Strip' …"

   [from the liner notes for *77 Sunset Strip*]

John **Barry**

On CD: The Living Daylights [soundtrack] (Warner Bros., 1987); Best of James Bond: 30th Anniversary Collection (EMI, 1992); Moviola (Sony, 1992); Until September/Car Crash (Silva Screen, 1992); Film Scores (Silva Screen, 1994); The EMI Years, Vol. 1 (Scamp, 1996); The EMI Years, Vol. 2 (Scamp, 1996); The EMI Years, Vol. 3 (Scamp, 1996); Moviola II: Action and Adventure (Sony, 1995); Octopussy [soundtrack] (Rykodisc, 1997); The Knack … and How to Get It [soundtrack] (Rykodisc-MGM, 1998)

Artie **Barsamian**
(and His Orchestra)

Count **Basie**
and His Orchestra

Ever wanted to hear Robert Conrad sing a tune from a Busby Berkeley musical? Well, that's just one of the treats waiting on the soundtrack LP from *Hawaiian Eye* (ABC-TV, 1959-63), with Conrad warbling "You're Getting to be A Habit with Me" from "42nd Street." Also on the disc: castmates Connie Stevens (singing "Let's Do It") and Poncie Ponce ("When My Dreamboat Comes Home"), along with lots of island-flavored TV jazz. As in most other p.i. series of the time, one of the settings was a lounge, the Shell Bar, where Ms. Stevens, as the chipper and lovely Cricket Blake, held forth at the mike.

– JW

Jo **Basile,** His Accordion
and Orchestra

Sid **Bass**

Les **Baxter**
(Les Baxter's Drums)

"Hell yeah, he was one of the architects of what became exotica. What he did went way beyond that. One thing, the first record released featuring the theremin, "Music Out of the Moon," was a Les Baxter record. It was also the first record with a full color cover. He was a pioneer in so many ways. He started out as a part of Mel Tormé's band. Everywhere you look in this field of music, Les Baxter did something important to pioneer it. Whatever corner you look, his stamp is there even if it is a little ways back. The first Martin Denny record was practically a Les Baxter cover album. Denny was more of a performer. Les was always behind the scene, behind a lot of scenes."

[Combustible Edison's The Millionaire, quoted in *Cheese Ball*]

Les is more

The many film scores of Les Baxter.

1953 – Tanga-Tika

1954 – The Yellow Tomahawk

1956 – The Black Sheep, Wetbacks, A Woman's Devotion, Hot Blood, Hot Cars, Quincannon, Frontier Scout, Rebel in Town

1957 – Bop Girl Goes Calypso, Girl in Black Stockings, Hell Bound, The Invisible Boy, Jungle Heat, Outlaw's Son, The Storm Rider, War Drums, Tomahawk Trail, Untamed Youth, Pharoah's Curse, Revolt at Fort Laramie, Voodoo Island

1958 – The Bride and the Beast, Escape from Red Rock, Fort Bowie, The Lone Ranger and the Lost City of Gold, Macabre

1960 – Goliath and the Barbarians (Italian production), House of Usher

1961 – Alakazam the Great (Japanese production), Black Sunday (Italian production), Goliath and the Dragon (Italian production), Lisette, Master of the World, The Pit and the Pendulum

1962 – Marco Polo (French/Italian production), Panic in the Year Zero!, Tales of Terror, White Slave Ship (French/Italian production)

1963 – X: The Man with the X-Ray

Eyes, Beach Party, Black Sabbath

(Italian production), Operation Bikini,

The Raven, Samson and the Seven

Miracles of the World, (French/Italian

production), The Young Racers

1964 – Bikini Beach, The Comedy of

Errors, Evil Eye (Italian production),

Muscle Beach Party, Pajama Party

1965 – Beach Blanket Bingo, Dr.

Goldfoot and the Bikini Machine,

How to Stuff a Wild Bikini, The

Mighty Jungle (U.S./Mexican pro-

duction), Sergeant Deadhead

1966 – Dr. Goldfoot and the Girl

Bombs (Italian production), Fireball

590, The Ghost in the Invisible Bikini

1968 – The Glass Sphinz

(Egyptian/Italian/Spanish produc-

tion), The Mini-Skirt Mob, Terror in

the Jungle, Wild in the Streets

1969 – Flareup, Hell's Belles

1970 – Cry of the Banshee (British

production), The Dunwich Horror

1972 – Baron Blood (Italian produc-

tion), Frogs

1973 – I Escaped from Devil's Island

1978 – Born Again

1980 – Target: Harry

1982 – The Beast Within

On CD: By Popular Request (Bacchus, 1996); Exotic Moods of Les Baxter [double disc] (Capitol,

1996); Les Baxter's Best (Capitol, 1996); For Dancers Only (CEMA, 1992); Love Is Blue (Crescendo, 1987); Colors of Brazil/African Blue (Crescendo, 1992); Brazil Now (Crescendo, 1993); The Lost Episode of Les Baxter (Dionysus, 1995); By Popular Request (Dionysus, 1996); Que Mango (Scamp, 1996) Master of the World (Varese Sarabande)

Francis **Bay** & His Orchestra With Strings

Swingin' Night People .... 5 - 3
(Omega OSL-50)

Harry **Belafonte**

Belafonte's Midnight Special *is hardly something very special, though this album does mark the first appearance on record of a harmonica player named Bob Dylan.*
– TC

Calypso .... 5 - 3
(RCA Victor LPM-1248, 1956)
Midnight Special .... 5 - 3
(RCA Victor LSP-2449, 1962)
Calypso In Brass .... 5 - 3
(RCA Victor LSP-3658, 1966)
Belafonte On Campus .... 5 - 3
(RCA Victor LPM-3779, 1967)
Belafonte Sings of Love .... 5 - 3
(RCA Victor LSP-3938, 1968)
In My Quiet Room [arranged by Hugo Montenegro] .... 5 - 3
(RCA Victor LSP-3571)
Many Moods of Belafonte .... 5 - 3
(RCA Victor LPM-2574)
Streets I Have Walked .... 5 - 3
(RCA Victor LPM-2695)
The Many Sides of Belafonte .... 5 - 3
(RCA Victor SP-33-92, 1960)

On CD: This Is Harry Belafonte (RCA, 1990); Island in the Sun (Pair, 1990); The Collection (RCA, 1991)

Tony **Bennett**

Treasure Chest of Song Hits .... 15 - 9
(Columbia CL-613, 1955)
Cloud Seven .... 15 - 9
(Columbia CL-621, 1955)

On CD: The Best of Tony Bennett (Capitol, 1991); 40 Years: The Artistry of Tony Bennett [boxed set] (Columbia-Legacy, 1991); Art of Excellence (Columbia, 1992); Perfectly Frank (Columbia, 1992); The Consummate Collection: Classic Songs … (Columbia, 1993); The Essence of Tony Bennett (Columbia, 1993); MTV Unplugged (Columbia, 1994); Here's to the Ladies (Columbia, 1995); Snowfall: The Tony Bennett Christmas Album (Columbia, 1995); I Left My Heart in San Francisco (Columbia); Movie Song Album (Columbia); The Classic Tony Bennett, Vol. 2 (Capitol, 1995); I Left My Heart in San Francisco/I Wanna Be Around (EMI, 1995); Isn't it Romantic? (MCA Special Products, 1995); My Romance (MCA Special Products, 1995); Singing & Swinging (Pilz, 1996); Steppin' Out (Sony, 1993); Something (Sony, 1995); My Best to You (Sony Special Products, 1995); All-Time Greatest Hits (Sony, 1997); Beat of My Heart (Sony, 1997); I Left My Heart in San Francisco/Art of Excellence/Astoria (Sony, 1997); Sings His All-Time Hall of Fame Hits (Sony, 1997); Songs for the Jet Set (Sony, 1997)

Frances **Bergen**

Candice's mom wasn't a half-bad lounge singer. In fact, she was pretty doggone good. In *The Beguiling Miss Frances Bergen*, she appears, variously, with Johnny Eaton's Quintet, the Matty Matlock Orchestra, and the Art Van Damme Quintet, performing a nice program of standards (and letting Van Damme cut loose with an instrumental, "Shivers"). As Jack Benny – *the* Jack Benny – puts it in his liner notes, "… that's the way Frances sings, soft, low, and sexy, going for nothing, but getting everything in return. Her voice is soothing, her interpretation unusual, and her phrasing fascinating." Thanks, Jack, for a dead-on description of the perfect female lounge singer.
– JW

The Beguiling Miss Frances Bergen .... 15 - 9
   (Columbia CL-873)

Elmer **Bernstein**

Often dismissed as a *Peter Gunn* knockoff, NBC-TV's *Johnny Staccato* (1959-60) certainly bore some similarities, including a jazz club (Waldo's, where the title character played piano between p.i. gigs) that served as a major setting, and a sharp score – composed, arranged and conducted by Leonard Bernstein – that expertly alternated between brassy and cool. Remarkably enough, *Johnny Staccato* (known simply as *Staccato* early on) would be the only TV series to feature famed actor John Cassavettes as a regular.
– JW

Staccato [soundtrack].. 20 - 12
   (Capitol ST-1287, 1959)
Paris Swings .... 20 - 12
   (Capitol ST-1288, 1960)
Caretakers .... 20 - 12
[soundtrack]
   (AVA AS-31, 1963)
The Great Escape .... 20 - 12
[soundtrack]
   (MGM, 1963)
Hawaii .... 20 - 12
[soundtrack]
   (United Artists UAL-4143, 1966)
The Man With the Golden Arm .... 20 - 12
[soundtrack]
   (Decca DL-8257)

On CD: The Great Escape [soundtrack] (Rykodisc, 1998); TV and Movie Themes (Mobile Fidelity); Collection: A Man and His Movies (Mainstream)

Stanley **Black**

On CD: Stanley Black Conducts (Alex, 1992)

Gerard **Blene**

"The time is the present. The place is everywhere. The mood is universal. The theme is love.

"The cast of two, a boy and a girl, are listening to a phonograph record when the curtain rises. The music fills the air as the drama unfolds. And although the lines have not yet been written, they've been said before. The music, however, brings to the dialogue new meaning, new depth and enough spark to rekindle the warm embers of romance.

"The play has been titled 'Time for Love.' The cast, the setting and the dialogue are inter-changeable but this romantic drama cannot be played without the musical setting supplied by Gerard Blene and his orchestra....

"For this is a romantic charade that demands something melodically correct and musically different. Yet not correct enough to lull or different enough to intrude. It may stay in keeping with the mood of the players and only attempt to heighten their emotions with subtle instrumental nuances.

"M. Blene has done just that. He know that this is a fragile drama which needs careful handling. A wrong move or a jarring note (musical, that is) can shatter the setting which was so carefully planned and bring down the curtain before the evening is over. He's like the wine steward who sees that the bottle is properly chilled or the head waiter who doesn't seat you behind a pole. He makes sure that there are no recriminations, no hurried exits, and no 'I'll hate myself in the morning' breast-beating by filling in with the kind of music that helps the players play at the game of love ..."

[from the Mike Gross liner notes for *Time for Love*]

Time for Love .... 5 - 3
   (Jubilee JGM-1029)

Bob & Ray

This unusual LP from the comedy pair of Bob and Ray features a musical extravaganza that technically should be filed under various artists. Dropping by for tuneful tidbits are Dick Schory, Lena Horne, George Melachrino, Skitch Henderson, Julie Andrews, Sauter-Finegan Orchestra and others.
– TC

Throw A Stereo Spectacular .... 5 - 3
   (RCA Victor LSP-1773, 1958)

Jean-Pierre **Bourtayre** and Jean **Bouchety**

The Game Is Over [soundtrack].. 5 - 3
   (ATCO 33-205, 1966)

Brasil '66, '77 or '86

[see Mendes, Sergio]

Harry **Breuer** and His Quintet

Mallet Mischief.. 5 - 3
   (Audio Fidelity, 1958)

Jean and Jean

Sometimes you wonder why there are people who collect albums for the jacket art instead of the music. Then you take a look at the Jane Fonda-Peter McEnery shot on the cover of the "The Game is Over" – whose soundtrack, created by a couple of French guys, is a blend of cool jazz, instrumental rock, solo sitar music, and, on a couple of tracks, a Tom Jones soundalike – and you begin to understand.

– JW

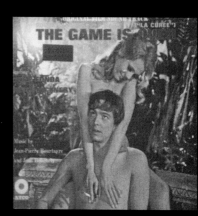

Ronnie **Brown**

Dave **Brubeck**

On CD: Jazz Impressions of New York (Columbia, 1990); Jazz Goes to College (Columbia, 1991); Plays and Plays and Plays (Original Jazz Classics); Greatest Hits (Sony, 1997); Time Out (Sony, 1997); Late Night Brubeck (Telarc, 1993); Nightshift (Telarc, 1993); Just You Just Me (Telarc, 1994); Young Lions & Old Tigers (Telarc, 1994); A Dave Brubeck Christmas (Telarc, 1996)

Jack **Burger**

Kenny **Burrell**

Joe **Bushkin**

The **Button-Down Brass**
(Ray Davies)

Jerry **Byrd**

Bobby **Byrne**

On CD: Amigo and Other Songs (Aurora, 1993); Soft Picks (Bainbridge, 1990); Best of Al Caiola (Aurora, 1995); Guitar of Plenty (Bainbridge, 1997); Soft Guitars (Bainbridge, 1997); Italian Guitars (Special Music, 1990)

Candido

On CD: Brujerias de Candido (Tico 1142, 1993)

Frank **Capp**

Frankie **Carle**
(His Piano and Orchestra)

"… Everything King Midas touched turned to gold. Inevitably, this got him into trouble because his power was disastrously all-inclusive. Luckily for Frankie Carle, his golden touch is restricted to music. It's only when he sits down at a piano that Mr. Carle's particular brand of magic makes itself known. Under his spell even an ordinary songs becomes something special, and sends a sort of golden glow through the room …"

[from Will MacFarland's liner notes for *The Golden Touch of Frankie Carle*]

Barbara **Carroll** Trio

David **Carroll**

Hey, Listen Baby – Let's Dance... 5-3
  (Mainstream 56095)
Waltzes, Wine, & Candlelight... 5-3
  (Mercury MG-20086)
Shimmering Strings 5-3
  (Mercury MG-20154)
Percussion in Hi-Fi 5-3
  (Mercury MG-20166, 1956)
The Feathery Feeling.. 5-3
  (Mercury MG-20286)
Dreams 5-3
  (Mercury MG-20301)
Repercussion 5-3
  (Mercury MG-20389)
Solo Encores... 5-3
  (Mercury SR-60180/MG 20503)
Mexico & 11 Other Great Hits 5-3
  (Mercury MG-20660)
Happy Feet.. 5-3
  (Mercury MG-20846)
House Party Discotheque with David Carroll 5-3
  (Mercury MG-20962)
Let's Dance.. 5-3
  (Mercury SR-60001, 1959)
The Feathery Feeling.. 5-3
  (Mercury SR-60026)
Dance and Stay Young.. 5-3
  (Mercury SR-60027)
Let's Dance Again 5-3
  (Mercury SR-60152, 1959)
Let's Dance, Dance, Dance.. 5-3
  (Mercury MG-20649/SR-60649)
Let's Dance to the Movie Themes 5-3
  (Mercury SR-60688)
Latin Percussion... 5-3
  (Mercury PPS-2000)
Percussion Orientale 5-3
  (Mercury PPS-2002)
Percussion Parisienne 5-3
  (Mercury MG 20955/PPS-2008)
Dance Date.. 5-3
  (Mercury MGW-12106)

"... For all we know, Adam and Eve may have engaged in a primitive form of the waltz or foxtrot. But although there are dances and dancing to fit every hour, the phrase "dancing in the dark" has a very special and intimate meaning all its own.

"Dancing in the dark is more exciting, more romantic, more inviting, more interesting, than dancing at other times. Your own imagination – as did Adam and Eve's, in all probability – can tell you why.

"Here, then, is a collection of melodies for dancing in the dark; familiar – yet ever new – love songs adapted by that master of the romantic keyboard, Carmen Cavallaro. It might not be inappropriate to suggest that you may even enjoy not dancing to these melodies ..."

[from the liner notes for *Dancing in the Dark*]

Benny **Carter**

Russ **Case** and His Orchestra

Don **Catelli** and the All Stars

Carmen **Cavallaro**

On CD: Christmas With Carmen Cavallaro (Peter Pan, 1995)

Frank **Chacksfield**

One of Duke Ellington's most famous compositions, the wonderful "Mood Indigo" has been recorded scores of times by all sorts of outfits. It has never, however, sounded better than on "Blue Rose," in which the twin voices of Rosemary Clooney and the Duke himself achieve an understated synergy that's the aural equivalent of a good martini's first icy bite.

— JW

George **Chakiris**

Pierre **Challet**

Clebanoff
(and His Orchestra)

Rosemary **Clooney**

"… Her long experience as a band singer, her admiration for Ellington and his music, and the special sort of supercharged satin in her voice all qualified her more than any other singer to make this unusual album …"
  [from the liner notes for *Blue Rose*]

On CD: Come on a My House (Bear Family, 1997); Christmas Classics (Chicago Music, 1995); The Essence of Rosemary Clooney (Columbia, 1993); 16 Most Requested Songs (Columbia); Do You Miss New York? (Concord Jazz, 1992); Still on the Road (Concord Jazz, 1993); White Christmas (Concord Jazz, 1996); Greatest Songs (Curb, 1996); More of the Best (Delta, 1996); Some of the Best (Delta, 1996); Everything's Rosie (Hindsight, 1995); Something to Remember Me By (Jasmine, 1997); Christmas (King, 1993); Swingin' Riddle (Koch, 1997); You Started Something (Sony Special Products, 1996); Songs from White Christmas and Other Yuletide Favorites (Sony, 1997); Best of Rosemary Clooney (Tristar, 1996); Love (Warner Bros., 1995)

The **Coctails**

On CD: Peel (Carrot Top, 1994); Early Hi-Ball Years (Carrot Top, 1995); Long Sound (Carrot Top, 1995); The Coctails (Carrot Top, 1996); Live at Lounge Ax (Carrot Top, 1996)

Buddy **Cole**

Cozy **Cole**

Nat 'King' **Cole**

Penthouse Serenade [10-inch] .... 50 - 30
  (Capitol H-332, 1952)
Lush Life .... 25 - 15
  (Capitol, 1952)
Unforgettable [10-inch] .... 35 - 21
  (Capitol T-357, 1953)
Unforgettable .... 20 - 12
  (Capitol T-357, 1953)
Unforgettable [reissue]... 5 - 3
  (Capitol ST/T-357, 1954)
Unforgettable [reissue]... 5 - 3
  (Capitol ST/T-357, 1965)
Unforgettable [reissue]... 5 - 3
  (Capitol 16162, 1981)
L-O-V-E .... 5 - 3
  (Capitol ST/T-2195)
Sings for Two in Love .... 20 - 12
  (Capitol, 1954)
Instrumental Classics .... 20 - 12
  (Capitol W-592, 1955)

The Piano Style of Nat "King" Cole .... 20 - 12
  (Capitol W-689, 1956)
Complete After Midnight Sessions.. 5 - 3
  (Capitol W-782)
Love Is the Thing... 5 - 3
  (Capitol W-824)
A Mis Amigos .... 20 - 12
  (Capitol 1220, 1959)
A Mis Amigos [reissue] .... 5 - 3
  (Capitol 11804, 1979)
A Mis Amigos [reissue] .... 5 - 3
  (Capitol 16137, 1980)
Ramblin' Rose .... 5 - 3
  (Capitol T/ST-1793)
Dear Lonely Hearts .... 5 - 3
  (Capitol T/ST-1838))

Nature Boy.. 5 - 3
  (Capitol T-2348, 1966)

On CD: The Piano Style of Nat "King" Cole (Blue Note, 1993); Complete After Midnight Sessions (Capitol, 1987); Unforgettable (Capitol, 1989); Unforgettable (Fat Boy, 1995); Lush Life (Capitol); Songs for Two in Love (Capitol); Billy May Sessions (Capitol, 1993)

Before scoring with such Broadway hits as "Sweet Charity" and "Barnum," on his way to becoming – as Time put it in a 1992 profile – "the last of Broadway's great composers," Cy Coleman was playing piano in trios at some of the snappier New York bistros. *Cool Coleman* features, among other treats, a nice piano-bar reading of "Witchcraft," one of the pianist's best-known compositions.

– JW

Cy **Coleman**

Combustible Edison

On CD: Blue Light (Domino [UK], 1993); I, Swinger (Sub Pop SP-244, 1994); Scizophonic (Sub Pop SP-313, 1996); Short Double Latte (Bungalo [Europe] BUNG-001, 1996); Soundtrack to "Four Rooms" (Elektra, 1995)

Perry **Como**

On CD: Christmas with Perry Como (BMG Special Products, 1997); Collection (Castle, 1992); Hello Young Lovers (Essex, 1993); Sings Just for You (Essex, 1996); Easy Listening (Pair); All-Time Greatest Hits, Vol. 1 (RCA, 1988); Pure Gold (RCA); Together at Christmas (RCA); Twenty Greatest Hits (RCA, 1990); My Greatest Songs (RCA, 1992); Yesterday & Today: A Celebration in Song [boxed set] (RCA, 1993); The Love Collection (RCA Camden, 1996); Sings Merry Christmas Music (Special Music, 1995); You Are Never Far Away (Special Music, 1996)

Ray **Conniff**

Ray Conniff's *We've Only Just Begun* looks and sounds like a typical Conniff offering, with tasteful, romantic versions of other people's hits and a highly attractive female face on the cover. The only two things that make it stand out are (1) the hot brunette pictured on the cover is his wife, Vera, and (2) Conniff himself poses on the back with a Ford Bronco racing car he drove in the 1970 Baja 500!

– JW

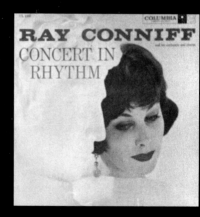

On CD: We Wish You a Merry Christmas (Columbia); Merry Christmas to All (Columbia); Christmas With Conniff (Columbia); Just Kiddin' Around (Sony, 1993); 40th Anniversary (Sony, 1995); 16 Most Requested Songs (Sony, 1995)

Don **Costa**

Music to Break a Sub-lease 5-3
   (ABC-Paramount ABC-212)
Come Shing With Ush 5-3
   (ABC-Paramount)
Echoing Voices and Trombones 5-3
   (United Artists WWS-8501)
The Sound of the Million Sellers 5-3
   (United Artists WWS-8513)

Jack **Costanzo**

Cha Cha Cha 5-3
   (Clarity 804)
Bongo Cha-Cha-Cha! 5-3
   (Evon 349)
Jack Costanzo and His Afro Cuban Band 5-3
   (GNP Crescendo GNP-19)
Vivo Tirado 5-3
   (GNP Crescendo GNPS-2057)
Latin Fever 5-3
   (Liberty LRP-3093, 1958)
Bongo Fever 5-3
   (Liberty LRP-3109)
Afro Can Can 5-3
   (Liberty LRP-3137, 1960)
Naked City 5-3
   (Liberty LST-7195)
Afro-Cuban Jazz North of the Border 5-3
   (Norgran MGN-32, 1954)
Mr. Bongo Afro Cuban Band 5-3
   (Palladium PLP-126, 1956)
Bongo Fever! 5-3
   (Sunset SUS-5134)
Mr. Bongo Plays in Hi-Fi 5-3
   (Tops 1564)
Afro-Cubano 5-3
   (Verve 8157, 1954)
Mr Bongo Has Brass 5-3
   (Zephyr 12003)

On CD: Afro Cuban (GNP Crescendo, 1998)

Budget labels were forever trying to slip something past the unwary consumer, and Diplomat Records may have been the best ever at it. In addition to the duplicitious Merseybeat cash-in, *Ringo's Theme (This Boy)* and *And I Love Her* by Al Goodman's Orchestra, there's *The Days of Wine and Roses,* as by Jesse Crawford, the well-known "poet of the organ." You have to read the small print on the cover to realize that the Poet of the Organ tickles the Hammond on only four of the 10 selections. The others are by an organist named Gayle Wilson. Hey, Gayle Wilson's no Jesse Crawford. But then again, it's unlikely that 99 out of 100 listeners could separate Crawford and Wilson's organ styles if you put a .44 Magnum to their heads. So where's the harm, really?

– JW

Irv **Cottler**

Around the World in Percussion .... 5 - 3
  (Somerset P-13900)

Roger **Coulam**

Hammond Stereo Sounds to Spoil You .... 5 - 3
  (Contour [UK] 6870524)

Jesse **Crawford**

Christmas With Hi-Fi Pipe Organ .... 5 - 3
  (Decca DL-8794)
The Days of Wine and Roses .... 5 - 3
  (Diplomat D-2319)
Organ Favorites .... 5 - 3
  (MCA)
Christmas With Jesse Crawford .... 5 - 3
  (MCA MCA-15013)

Bob **Crewe**
(Bob Crewe Generation)

You can find Bob Crewe, creator of the notorious "Music to Watch Girls By," behind the production of numerous Four Seasons records.

Music to Watch Girls By .... 5 - 3
  (Dynovoice 9003, 1967)
Motivation .... 5 - 3
  (Elektra 7E-1103, 1977)
Street Talk .... 5 - 3
  (Elektra 7E-1083)
Kicks .... 5 - 3
  (Warwick WST-2009, 1966)
Crazy in the Heart .... 5 - 3
  (Warwick W-2034, 1967)

Bing **Crosby**

"Honestly, I can't jump up and down and make a great foo-foo-raw over the singing, but I do maintain that Nelson has produced some very lush and memorable sounds, and the songs certainly have great appeal."
  [from Bing Crosby's liner notes for *Return to Paradise Islands*]

Nobody sings like Bing

*The incomparable
Bing Crosby.*

Rhino Records

On CD: On the Sentimental Side (ASV/Living Era, 1992); Blue Hawaii (Axis EMI, 1993); Bing Crosby's Christmas Classics (Capitol); Collection (Castle, 1992); Christmas Wishes (Cema Special Markets, 1995); Christmas With Bing Crosby, Nat King Cole and Dean Martin (Cema Special Markets, 1995); Moonlight Becomes You (Charly, 1994); Bing Crosby the Crooner: The Columbia Years [boxed set] (Columbia, 1988); 16 Most Requested Songs; (Columbia, 1992); The Complete United Artists Sessions White Christmas [soundtrack] (LaserLight); Bing Crosby Sings Again (MCA, 1986); Greatest Hits (MCA, 1995); That Christmas Feeling (MCA Special Products, 1995); The Bing Crosby Years [boxed set] (MCA, 1994); Bing's Gold Records (MCA, 1997); Love Songs (MCA Special Products, 1997); My Favorite Hawaiian Songs (MCA Special Products, 1997); Bing Crosby's Greatest Hits (MCA); Blue Skies (MCA); Holiday Inn (MCA); The Movie Hits (Pearl, 1992); Swingin' on a Star (Pearl, 1995); Christmas with Bing Crosby & Frank Sinatra (Pilz, 1996); Pennies From Heaven (Pro Arte); World of Bing Crosby: On Sentimental Side (Sound Solution, 1993); Happy Holidays (Special Music, 1992); The Christmas Songs (Vintage Jazz, 1990)

Xavier **Cugat**
and His Orchestra

When Xavier Cugat retired in 1970, he turned over his orchestra to Tito Puente.

On CD: Adios Muchachos (Pro Arte, 1992); Me Gusta La Conga (Saludos Amigos, 1993); Negro Zumbon [with Abbe Lane and Tito Puente] (Saludos Amigos, 1993); 16 Most Requested Songs (Columbia, 1993); Rumba Rumbero (Tumbao, 1995); Xavier Cugat and His Orchestra, 1944-1945 (Circle, 1995); Congas, Chihuahuas and Rhumbas, 1940-1945 (Harlequin, 1996); Early Years (Harlequin, 1996); Xavier Cugat and His Orchestra (Saludos Amigos, 1994); Mambo No. 4 (Columbia, 1995); Golden Classics (Collectibles, 1995); Cugat's Favorite Rhumbas: Leyendas/Legends (Sony International, 1995); Say Si Si (Pair, 1995); Latinissimo (Madacy, 1995); Unheard Transcriptions and Air Shots (Harlequin, 1995); Latin Dance Time With Xavier Cugat and His Orchestra (Fat Boy, 1996); Cugie A-Go-Go (MCA, 1997); Cuban Love Song (Harlequin, 1997); New Xavier Cugat Orchestra: Hot! Hot! Hot! (Laserlight); Latin for Lovers (Essex)

Bobby **Darin**

Lew **Davies**

Ray **Davies**

[see Button-Down Brass, The]

**Darin
do**

Bobby Darin died of heart disease at the tender age of 37.

From Sinatra manque to jeans jacket-wearing protest singer, Bobby Darin *covered the '60s like a sharkskin suit. No one else went from starring in musicals with Sandra Dee to singing about convicts onstensibly murdered by the state of Arkansas.*

Sammy **Davis** Jr.

On CD: The Wham of Sam (Warner Archives, 1995); What Kind of Fool Am I and Other Show-Stoppers (Pair, 1993); Sammy Davis Jr. Sings, Laurindo Almeida Plays (DCC, 1997); Sounds of '66 (DCC, 1996); Decca Years (MCA, 1990); Sammy Davis Jr. (Huub, 1991); Sings Great Country Hits (Huub, 1991); What I've Got in Mind (Charly Budget, 1995); All the Things You Are (Pair-MCA-Essex, 1996); That Old Black Magic (MCA) Greatest Hits, Vol. 2 (DCC) Greatest Hits, Vols. 1 and 2 (DCC); Greatest

Hits, Vol. 1 (Garland); Best of Sammy Davis Jr. (Capitol-Curb, 1991); Great Sammy Davis Jr. (Columbia, 1989); Capitol Collectors Series (Capitol, 1990); Greatest Songs (Capitol-Curb, 1990); Greatest Hits (Huub, 1991); Collection (Castle, 1992); Greatest Hits Live (Curb, 1995); I've Gotta Be Me: The Best of Sammy Davis Jr. on Reprise (Reprise, 1996); Golden Boy [soundtrack] (Bay Cities-Angel)

Lenny **Dee**

Golden Organ Favorites .... 5 - 3
   (Decca DL-4112/74112)
Golden Organ Favorites [reissue] .... 5 - 3
   (MCA MCA-182, 1971)
Happy Holi-Dee .... 5 - 3
   (Decca DL-74146)
By Popular Dee-Mand .... 5 - 3
   (Decca DL-4429/74429)
Something Special .... 5 - 3
   (Decca DL-74498)
Lenny Dee in Hollywood! .... 5 - 3
   (Decca DL-74315)
Most Requested .... 5 - 3
   (Decca DL-74572)
Sweethearts on Parade .... 5 - 3
   (Decca DL-4632/74632)
The Lenny Dee Tour .... 5 - 3
   (Decca DL-74654)
My Favorite Things .... 5 - 3
   (Decca DL-4706)
Gentle on My Mind .... 5 - 3
   (Decca DL-74994)
Turn Around Look at Me .... 5 - 3
   (Decca DL-75073)
Spinning Wheel .... 5 - 3
   (Decca DL-75152)
Mellow-Dee .... 5 - 3
   (Decca DL-78796)
Lenny Dee Plays the Hits .... 5 - 3
   (Decca DL-78857)
The Lenny Dee Show .... 5 - 3
   (Decca DL-78913)
In the Mood .... 5 - 3
   (Decca DL-74818)
Moving On .... 5 - 3
   (Decca DL-74880)
Relaxin' .... 5 - 3
   (Decca DL-4946/74946)

Martin **Denny**

"Hawaii has always been a place of excitement, but an excitement of a different kind, associated mainly with swaying palms, steel guitars and beautiful brown-skinned girls. Now they also have the Go-Go and it's just as fast, frantic and exciting as it is anywhere. On this recording, Martin Denny proves it to the hilt; encouraged by the enthusiasm of the crowd, he swings and rocks through some of the top Hawaiian hits associated with his name to give you the beat of the frug, monkey, watusi, etc. On everyone of the selections you will hear the "hip"-notic fenzie and handclapping excitement from the enthusiastic crowd. The spirit of this dancing crowd will likewise catch you when you hear the tunes."

[from the liner notes to *Hawaii Goes a Go-Go*]

"There is no doubt that this is the Go-Go generation. The words Go-Go have become an automatic phrase of this era. There's everything from Go-Go discotheques to Go-Go laundromats and, I am sure, many people have asked themselves "Where does this all come from?" It all started in Paris, France and spread like wildfire to both the east and the west. It has traveled across oceans and plains to such far corners as Finland, Japan and South America. Hawaii is certainly not one to be left behind ..."

[from the liner notes for *Hawaii Goes a Go-Go*]

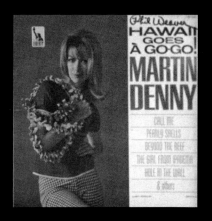

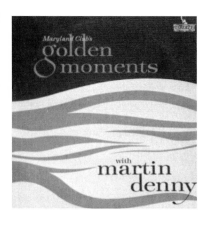

Maryland Club's Golden Moments With Martin Denny 20-12
   (Liberty)
Paradise Moods 15-9
   (Sunset SUS-5102)
Sayonara 25-15
   (Sunset SUS-5199)
The Very Best of Martin Denny 10-6
   (United Artists)

On CD: Exotica 90 ([Japan] TCP-6160); Afro-desia (Scamp SCP 9702-2, 1996); Exotica! The Best of Martin Denny (Rhino R2 70774, 1990); Afro-Desia (Scamp, 1995); Exotica I & II (Scamp, 1996); Forbidden Island & Primitiva (Scamp, 1996); Hypnotique & Exotica 3 (Scamp, 1997); Paradise (Pair, 1988); Exotic World Of Martin Denny (REV-OLA, 1995); Bachelor in Paradise (Pair, 1996); The Exciting Sounds of Martin Denny: Exotica (Scamp, 1996); The Exotic Sounds of Martin Denny (Capitol, 1996); Greatest Hits (Curb, 1994); Quiet Village/The Enchanted Sea (Scamp, 1997)

Derek & Ray

Interplay 5-3
   (RCA Victor LSP-3530, 1966)

Leo Diamond

Exciting Sounds from Romantic Places 5-3
   (ABC-Paramount ABC/ABCS-268)
Subliminal Sounds 5-3
   (ABC-Paramount ABCS-303)
Ebb Tide 5-3
   (Harmony HS-11328)
Skin Diver Suite 5-3
   (RCA Victor LPM-116)
The Harmonica Magic of Leo Diamond 5-3
   (RCA Victor LPM-1042)
Snuggled On Your Shoulder 5-3
   (RCA Victor LPM-1442)
Hi-Fi Harmonica 5-3
   (Roulette R-25019, 1958)
Exciting Sounds of the South Seas 5-3
   (Reprise R9-6002)
Themes from the Great Foreign Films 5-3
   (Reprise R9-6009)
Off Shore 5-3
   (Reprise R9-6024)

Directional Sound

Robert **Drasnin**

Robert Drasnin was known chiefly for his television themes – "Lost in Space," "Man From U.N.C.L.E.," "Playhouse 90," etc. He only had one album as a solo leader, and it was released both as Voodoo *and* Percussion Exotique.
– TC

On CD: Voodoo (Dionysus-Bacchus BA-09, 1996)

Peter **Duchin**

On CD: Dance With Peter Duchin (Fiction-Fortune 2994)

Johnny **Duffy**

Johnny Duffy revered the king of instruments so much that he built his life around one. Well, his house, anyway. His Liberty album, An Excursion in Hi-Fi, *comes with a booklet describing how he designed and built a house around a 1929 Wurlitzer Theater Organ. Think of the parties he had!*
– TC

The **Electro-Sonic** Orchestra
(conducted by Dick Jacobs)

Les **Elgart** and
His Orchestra

On CD: Ain't We Got Fun (Drive Archive, 1995); The Elgart Touch/For Dancers Also (Collector's Choice)

Les and Larry **Elgart**

On CD: Les and Larry Elgart (Columbia, 1990); Sophisticated Swing (Columbia, 1992); Greatest Dance Band in the Land (Columbia Special Products, 1995); Latin Obsession [Larry] (Columbia International 80040)

Duke **Ellington**

Duke Ellington was not a lounge artist, but few of the wacky instrumental bandleaders that

came of age in the era of stereo could have had so much fun without Ellington's pioneering spirit. Ellington, an accomplished piano player, saw his orchestra as his instrument. With the assistance of composer-arranger Billy Strayhorn, Ellington wrote not for the instruments in his orchestra but for the individual players. Getting to know their strengths and weaknesses, he catered his compositions to their styles – Bubber Miley's expertise with a trumpet plunger, "Tricky" Sam Nanton's proficiency with a wah-wah trombone. Early on, this gave his orchestras a confident and playful sound. Realizing all the abilities at hand, Ellington could use them to a greater effect, channelling their styles into a larger sound – often something other than merely musical. As early as the 1930s, he was using his orchestra to mimic sounds from the world around him. "Daybreak Express," for instance, is an amazing imitation of a train using the entire orchestra. Without this early trail-blazing sonic experimentation, it's hard to believe that the wowee zounds of everyone from Dean Elliott to Esquivel would have been as easily braved. – TC

On CD: Afro-Bossa (Discovery, 1992)

Dean **Elliott** and His Swinging Big, Big Band

Don **Elliott** & Orchestra

Ray **Ellis**

"Within the wall of this album cover are musical sounds of the future. Music for the next decade ... A step beyond progressive jazz, a subtle sound of mood music prevails. Here are magnificent rounded modern interpretations of great songs with the finest array of musicians this side of 'Sputnik.'

"A handsome young man enters the recording studio embodying all the appearance and traits of the typical 'on campus' American youth. He quietly sheds his coat and starts to set up his mellophone, vibes, bongos , trumpet ... then he positions the celeste setting the piano stool for comfort. Out comes his horned rimmed glasses to check the music and you think of the successful young junior executive. Where is the musician Don Elliott? ... man ... he's here!"

[from Abbot Lutz's liner notes for *Music of the Sensational Sixties*]

At the Chicago Sun-Times, there was a very influential columnist named Sig Sakowitz. He wrote the entertainment column, where he would critique everyone playing in town. Before we opened [at the Empire Room in the Parkman House Hotel] he wrote in his column "Esquivel! ... Why?" He came to the show, and I showed him why. He came almost every night. The next week in his column he wrote, "Esquivel is so good he deserves 2 exclamation points."

[Juan Esquivel, July 1995]

The dashing Juan Esquivel.

Emery

Juan Garcia **Esquivel**

For those of you who do not speak Spanish, I could tell you that the name Esquivel, translated into English, means "Exciting," or "enchanting," or "exotic," or "effervescent," "ebullient," or even "electric," and any one of these words might be true. As a matter of fact, they are all true when we speak about Juan Garcia Esquivel in any or all of his roles as composer, arranger, pianist, conductor, or in his complete personality as a man.

[from the Stanley Wilson liner notes for *More of Other Worlds, Other Sounds*]

If you want a perfect example of the romantic-escapist nature of the best lounge music, look no further than "Passport to Romance" by Percy Faith, one of the true masters of easy-listening. Gaze at the album jacket as you listen to these exotic instrumental themes, this traveling music for lovers. Doesn't the girl look wildly alive and exhilarated as she waves goodbye to her envious friends? Doesn't the guy look dapper and ready for adventure in strange ports-of-call? Don't you just know they'll be humping like minks before they're even out of the channel?

– JW

On CD: Space-Age Bachelor Pad Music (Bar/None, 1994); More of Other Worlds, Other Sounds (Reprise Archives , 1995); Music From a Sparkling Planet (Bar/None, 1995); Cabaret Manana (RCA, 1995); Merry Xmas From the Space Age Bachelor Pad (Bar/None, 1996); Other Worlds, Other Sounds/Four Corners of the World (Bar/None, 1997); Exploring New Sounds in Stereo/Strings Aflame (Bar/None, 1997); Infinity in Sounds, Vols. 1 and 2 (Bar/None, 1997); Latinesque/See It in Sound (Bar/None, 1997); The Genius of Esquivel/Esquivel!! (Bar/None, 1997); To Love Again/Early Mexican Recordings (Bar/None, 1997)

Percy **Faith**

On CD: Christmas Is (Columbia, 1989); Latin Themes for Young Lovers (Sony, 1990); Night Before Christmas (Delta, 1992); Deep Purple (Special Music, 1993); Latin Rhythms (Ranwood, 1995); Hollywood's Greatest Themes (Sony Special Products, 1995); Joy to the World (Sony Special Products, 1995); Songs From Award-Winning Movies (Ranwood, 1996); Back to Back (K-Tel, 1997); Great Movie Themes (Ranwood, 1997); Fascination (Sony Special Products, 1995); Music of Christmas (Columbia); Greatest Hits (Columbia)

Frances **Faye**

No Reservations [10-inch].. 5 - 3
    (Capitol H-512, 1954)
Caught in the Act .... 5 - 3
    (Crescendo GNPS-92, 1958)
Frances Faye in Frenzy .... 5 - 3
    (Verve MGV-2147, 1961)
Swinging All the Way With Frances Faye .... 5 - 3
    (Verve V6-8434, 1962)

On CD: Caught in the Act (Crescendo, 1994)

Sid **Feller**

Music to Break a Lease By .... 5 - 3
    (ABC-Paramount ABC-107)
More Music to Break a Lease .... 5 - 3
    (ABC-Paramount ABCS-416)

Ferrante and Teicher

Ferrante and Teicher With Percussion .... 5 - 3
    (ABC/Paramount ABCS-248, 1958)
Heavenly Sounds in Hi-Fi .... 5 - 3
    (ABC-Paramount ABC-221)
Postcards From Paris .... 5 - 3
    (ABC-Paramount ABCS-430)
Twin Piano Magic of Ferrante & Teicher Vol. 1 .... 5 - 3
    (ABC-Paramount ABCS-557)
Nostalgic Hits From the Twin Pianos of Ferrante & Teicher [double album] ...... 5 - 3
    (ABC ABCX-791-2, 1973)
Blast Off! .... 5 - 3
    (ABC-Paramount ABCS-285, 1959)
At the Movies .... 5 - 3
    (Capitol 9105)
Hi-Fireworks .... 5 0 - 30
    (Columbia CL-573)
Broadway to Hollywood .... 5 - 3
    (Columbia CS-8407, 1960)
Golden Piano Hits .... 5 - 3
    (Liberty LT-506269)
In Love With.. 5 - 3
    (Pickwick SPC-3077)
Golden Piano Hits .... 5 - 3
    (United Artists UAS-6269/WWS-8505)

"*Concert for Lovers* can very well describe any sitting in which Arthur Ferrante and Lou Teicher are supplemented by a lush orchestra backdrop. The popular piano team are the Fort Knox of the record business. The gold bricks in Fort Knox set the standard for our economy and the golden touch in their hands sets the standard of our music ..."

[from Mike Gross' liner notes for *Concert for Lovers*]

Not long ago, a lady walked past a tall building in New York City, looked up and, forgetting her ladylike composure, did a quick double-take. What she saw was a huge grand piano scampering up the side of the building, quickly followed by another. Any self-respecting hi-fi or stereo fan could have told her that Ferrante and Teicher were in town.

[from Rick Ward's liner notes to *Blast Off!*]

You'll find the name of composer, arranger, and jazz harpist Robert Maxwell in several places throughout this book. Writer of both the pop classic "Ebb Tide" and the evergreen "Shangri-La" (the latter a Top 20 pop hit in 1964 for his own orchestra), he shows up in an unlikely place with "Songs of the Nairobi Trio."

The Trio, of course, was the creation of the visionary comic Ernie Kovacs. In it, three people in ape suits (usually including Kovacs and wife Edie Adams) came out and

[continued on next page]

Postcards From Paris .... 75 - 45
    (Westminster WP-6001)
Adventures in Carols .... 75 - 45
    (Westminster WP-6021, 1954)
Xmas Hi-Fi Favorites [10-inch] .... 75 - 45
    (Westminster WL-3044, 1954)

On CD: Easy Listening Favorites [abridged Heavenly Sounds in Hi-Fi] (MCA Special Products, 1993); A Foggy Day (Liberty, 1990); Snowbound/We Wish You a Merry Christmas (Capitol, 1992); All Time Great Movie Themes (Capitol, 1993); Easy Listening Favorites (MCA Special Products, 1993); Dos Piano Latinos (Laserlight, 1995); Winter Wonderland (Laserlight, 1995); Autumn Leaves (Sony Special Products, 1995); Hot Latin Nights (Intersound, 1995); Blast Off (Varese Sarabande, 1997); Two Pianos in Italy (LaserLight); The Best of Ferrante & Teicher [double album] (United Artists, 1973); Greatest Hits (Curb); All-Time Favorite Hits (CEMA, 1992); 40th Anniversary Collector's Edition (Intersound, 1992); The Greatest Love Songs of All (Pair, 1995); All Time Greatest Hits (Capitol, 1995); The Collection (Varese Sarabande, 1998)

Art **Ferrante**

On CD: Ferrante and the Phantom (Bainbridge, 1989); Ferrante and Kris Kringle (Bainbridge, 1989); Touch of Art (Pro Arte, 1991); Christmas With Ferrante/The Sonset Park Choir (Intersound International, 1992)

Chucho **Ferrer** /
Mario Ruiz Armengol

Mood Music in the Latin Manner .... 5 - 3
    (RCA Victor CSP-103, 1962)

George **Feyer**

A Nightcap With George Feyer .... 5 - 3
    (Decca DL-74625/DL-4625)

Irving **Fields**

Pizzas and Bongos .... 5 - 3
    (Decca DL-74175)
Champagne and Bongos .... 5 - 3
    (Decca DL-74238)
Bikinis and Bongos .... 5 - 3
    (Decca DL-74323)
Bagels and Bongos .... 5 - 3
    (Decca DL-78856)

Jack **Fina**

Ralph **Font**
(and His Orchestra)

The **Fortune Tellers**

Connie **Francis**

On CD: White Sox, Pink Lipstick and Stupid Cupid [boxed set] (Bear Family, 1993); Greatest Hits (K-Tel, 1994); Solid Gold (Pair)

played amusingly syncopated pop songs, often using their mallets on one another. The instrumental single *Song of the Nairobi Trio,* by the Fortune Tellers, made a good enough run at the charts in '61 to lead to an LP, featuring goofy little Maxwell arrangements of such material as "Deep in the Heart of Texas," "Ah! Sweet Mystery of Life" and the music for Hamms Beer commercials running groove to groove with Maxwell-penned originals like "Nairobi Moonlight" and "Home on the Range Twist."

– JW

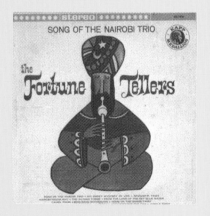

The **Frederico Strings** and Orchestra

Twilight Hour... 5 - 3
    (Kapp, KL-1010)

Dom (Dominic) **Frontiere**

The Mighty Accordion Band.. 5 - 3
    (Capitol ST-1212)
Pagan Festival: An Exotic Love Ritual for Orchestra .... 5 - 3
    (Columbia CL-1273)
Love Eyes: The Moods of Romance .... 5 - 3
    (Columbia CS-8224)
Dom Frontiere and His El Dorado.. 5 - 3
    (Liberty LJH-6002)
Mr. Accordion.. 5 - 3
    (Liberty LST-7008)
Fabulous.. 5 - 3
    (Liberty LST-7015)

Serge **Gainsbourg**

Du Chant a la Une!... 200 - 120
    (1958)
L'etonnant Serge Gainsbourg .... 50 - 30
    (1961)
Gainsbourg Confidentiel .... 50 - 30
    (1964)
Histoire de Melody Nelson .... 50 - 30
    (1971)

On CD: Couleur Café (Philips/Mercury, 1996); Comic Strip (Philips/Mercury, 1996); Du Jazz Dans Le Ravin (Philips/Mercury, 1996); Je T'aime Moi (Musicrama, 1994); Aux Armes Et Cetera (Polydor, 1996); Histoire de Melody Nelson (Polydor, 1996); Homme a Tete de Chou (Polydor, 1996); Mauvaises Nouvelles des Etoiles (Polydor, 1996); Rock Around the Bunker (Polydor, 1996); Vue de L'exterieur (Polydor, 1996); Theatre le Palace '80 (Polydor, 1998); Master Series: The Best of Serge Gainsbourg (Polydor, 1998); Gainsbourg a Gainsbarre (Polydor, 1998)

Pedro **Garcia** and His Del Prado Orchestra

Tropical Cruise .... 5 - 3
    (Audio Fidelity AFLP-1041)

Russ **Garcia**

Erroll **Garner**

On CD: Mambo Moves Garner (Mercury, 1991); Now Playing/A Night at the Movies/Up in Erroll's Room (Telarc); Encores in Hi-Fi (Tristar, 1994)

Tommy **Garrett**
(50 Guitars of Tommy Garrett)

One of the great novelty records of all time, *Seymour Gibbons Plays With Himself,* at first appears to be simply an album of double-tracked piano with drums and bass and an unfortunate title. But those picking up the album with an air of jaded superiority, figuring it to be unintentional camp from another era, soon realize the joke's on them. From the song titles – "Lovely Way to Spend an Evening," "I Get Along Without You Very Well" – to the raves from bogus critics on the back ("A real comer!" "Stimulating performance capped by an unbelievable climax!"), this is a wildly amusing package that must've caused more than a few people to bust a gut when it first came out.

The piano work isn't half-bad, either, although the zipper noises that open and close each song can be a little distracting.

– JW

On CD: The Artistry of Stan Getz: Best of the Verve Years (Verve, 1991); Stan Getz With Cal Tjader (Original Jazz Classics, 1991); Getz Au Go Go Featuring Astrud Gilberto (Verve); Getz/Gilberto, Vol. 2 (Verve); Big Band Bossa Nova (Verve); Jazz Samba (Verve, 1992; DCC, 1994; PolyGram, 1997); Getz/Gilberto (Verve, 1992; PolyGram, 1997); Stan Getz with Guest Artist Laurindo Almeida (Verve)

Seymour **Gibbons**

Jackie **Gleason**

"Sensuous, sophisticated ... a new musical concept that embodies the luxurious richness of velvet and the masculine brilliance of bright burnished brass.

"Smoothly directing an orchestra that features trumpets, trombones and French horns, Jackie Gleason creates an album of subdued contrasts in brass. Embellished with a danceable beat and a solo sax, the music displays the unique Gleason talent for blending unusual instrumentations with the warmth and tenderness of a beautiful song."
[liner notes for *Jackie Gleason Presents Velvet Brass*]

"Music, martinis, and memories ... each creates a wonderfully soft, romantic haze. Put them all together and you have a very special effect – a mood whose warmth and tenderness are irristibly appealing ... "
[from the liner notes for *Jackie Gleason Presents Music, Martinis and Memories*]

"Into this intensely romantic album, Jackie Gleason has decanted a tranquilizing potion as dreamily hypnotic as a warm breeze caressing a field of poppies ..."
[from the liner notes for *Opiate d'Amour*]

Known to most of America as a beloved T.V. clown (*The Jackie Gleason Show, The Honeymooners*), the rotund comedy master Jackie Gleason earned a secondary reputation as a conductor and occasional composer of music best heard behind the tinkling of champagne glasses, or the crinkling of sheets. The Gleason discs often include a few Jackie originals; *Opiate d'Amour,* for instance, features an incredibly moody reading of "Melancholy Serenade," his longtime theme song and best - known composition, along with five other Gleason-penned numbers.

– JW

FULL DIMENSIONAL STEREO

JACKIE GLEASON

PRESENTS

Music for Lovers Only

The cover photo to Gleason's *Music, Martinis and Memories* expertly sums up those 1,000 words needed to explain or define lounge music. A woman sits at a bar with a pianist in the background. That's enough, right? No, it's more than that. Anyone who picked up this book knows that lounge music is more than just kitsch with a chaser. Look at this woman. She's dressed to the nines, she's nearly finished her drink, and she's alone at that bar. She's not putting on airs and struggling to be radiant – in fact, the camera has caught her in a moment with her defenses down. She's staring into space. She's thinking. No – she's remembering. Remembering what? An old flame? The way it used to be? Younger days? Whatever it is, it's more serious than a simple whiff of nostalgia – it's a memory that still has a grip on her heart. What brought on this memory, the one the struggles to be radiant are meant to suppress? The music. That faceless pianoman over her shoulder. The half-forgotten tune broke through her defenses and now parades through her mind. She's in the lounge – literally and figuratively – and she's not alone.

Thomas Conner

On CD: The Romantic Moods of Jackie Gleason (Capitol CD-7243); And Away We Go! [TV performances] (Scamp, 1996); Merry Christmas (Capitol, 1990); Merry Christmas (Razor and Tie, 1995); Velvet Brass (Capitol, 1983); Lush Moods (Pair, 1984); Music, Martinis and Memories (Capitol, 1988); Happy Holidays (CEMA, 1992); 'Tis the Season (Capitol, 1993); Body and Soul (Pair, 1995); And Awaaay We Go! (Scamp, 1996); Romantic Moods of Jackie Gleason (Capitol, 1996); For the Quiet Hours (CEMA); Tenderly (CEMA); For Lovers Only [triple disc] (CEMA); Music for Lovers Only (Capitol); Shangri-La (Pair); Best of Jackie Gleason (Capitol-Curb, 1993); Home for the Holidays [with Al Martino] (CEMA, 1995); How Sweet It Is! The Jackie Gleason Velvet Brass (Razor and Tie, 1996); Night Winds/Music to make You Misty (Capitol, 1991)

Marty **Gold**

"Soloists and entire sections of the orchestra appear to move thrillingly back and forth across the room. Stereo Action is musical movement so real, your eyes will follow the sound."
   [from the liner liner notes for *Stereo Action*]

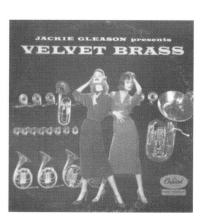

Besides a line reading "This Is Not the Original Sound Track," the subtitle for Al Goodman's *Ringo's Theme (This Boy) and And I Love Her* is "Plus Other Beautiful String Themes." According to the album's back cover, those other beautiful string themes include "Liverpool Theme," "We Love You" and "Those Boys From England."

But woe to the Beatles-crazed boy or girl who popped the buck or so for this budget-label offering. After passable instrumental versions of the two Beatles songs that comprise the album's title, the rest of the LP is given over to schmaltzy

Al **Goodman**
(and His Orchestra)

Ringo's Theme (This Boy) and And I Love Her.. 5 - 3
   (Diplomat DS-2336)

Ron **Goodwin**

It Can't Be Wrong... 5 - 3
   (Capitol T-10078)
Music For An Arabian Night... 5 - 3
   (Capitol T-10251)

On CD: Golden Sounds of Ron Goodwin and His Orchestra (Disky, 1996); Conducts TV and Film Scores (Flyback, 1998)

Bobby **Gordon**

Young Man's Fancy.. 5 - 3
   (Decca DL-74507/4507)

Eydie **Gormé**

[see also Lawrence, Steve and Eydie Gormé]

Blame It on the Bossa Nova.. 5 - 3
   (Columbia CL-2012/CS-8812, 1963)
Let the Good Times Roll.. 5 - 3
   (Columbia CL-2065/CS-8865, 1963)
Amor.. 5 - 3
   (Columbia CL-2203/CS-9003, 1964)
More Amor... 5 - 3
   (Columbia CL-2376/CS-9176, 1965)
Eydie Gormé's Greatest Hits .... 5 - 3
   (Columbia CL-2764/CS-9564, 1967)
Eydie Gormé.. 5 - 3
   (Paramount S-150, 1957)
Come Sing With Me.. 5 - 3
   (United Artists UAL-3143/UAS-6143, 1961)
The Very Best of Eydie Gormé .... 5 - 3
   (United Artists UAL-3189/UAS-6189, 1962)

On CD: Eydie Gormé (Taragon, 1995); Best of Eydie Gormé (DJ Specialist, 1997)

romantic string-laden evergreens, masquerading under new titles in an unvarnished effort to fleece a few kids, or their parents. (The tune called "London" on the label, for instance, is actually "Stranger in Paradise"!) Certainly unethical, and probably at least mildly illegal, this deception gave rise to what is certainly one of the oddest of the lounge albums, part moptop and part Mantovani, a calculated cash-in that (barely) delivered what it promised, and gave untold of Fab Four fans a big old surprise in the bargain.

– JW

"The witching hour of midnight has an atmosphere all its own, and of all the arts music is best fitted to express its poetic mood.

"Here the brilliant American composer and conductor, Morton Gould, has selected, arranged and conducted eight songs that in this orchestral guise breathe the mystery, the passion and the beauty of the haunting hour."

[from the liner notes for *Music at Midnight*]

Morton **Gould**

The mood is mod ... Morton Gould a la mod.
Here the maestro is in a mod, mod, mod, mod whirl inspired by the rocking rhythms and swinging songs–the hit songs – of the "now" generation ... the Junioration.
[from the liner notes for *Morton Gould Makes the Scene*]

Morton Gould Makes the Scene .... 5 - 3
 (RCA Victor LSP-37711)

On CD: Brass and Percussion (RCA, 1993); Tribute (Troy, 1996); Jungle Drums (RCA, 1996); Kern and Porter Favorites (RCA, 1996); Moon, Wind and Stars (RCA, 1996); Musical Christmas Tree (RCA)

Steve **Graham**
(Steve Graham Strings)

Music for Those Who Go Steady .... 5 - 3
 (Warner Bros. WS-1437, 1962)

Earl **Grant**

Grant Takes Rhythm .... 5 - 3
 (Decca DL7-8905, 1959)
Ebb Tide .... 5 - 3
 (Decca DL-74165/DL-4165)
Trade Winds .... 5 - 3
 (Decca DL-74623/DL-4623)
Beyond the Reef .... 5 - 3
 (Decca DL-74231)
Earl Grant at Basin Street .... 5 - 3
 (Decca DL-74299)
Fly Me to the Moon .... 5 - 3
 (Decca DL-74454)
Just for a Thrill .... 5 - 3
 (Decca DL-74506)
Gently Swingin' .... 5 - 3
 (Decca DL-74937)
Spanish Eyes .... 5 - 3
 (Decca DL-74974)
Winter Wonderland .... 5 - 3
 (MCA MCA-15001)
The End .... 5 - 3
 (MCA MCA-20270)

On CD: The End (Alex, 1993)

George **Greeley**

The Most Beautiful Music of Hawaii .... 15 - 9
 (Warner Bros. WS-1366)

Certainly, not all of famed organist Ken Griffin's oeuvre belongs here: There's *Skating Time* (Columbia, CL 610), for instance, which features tunes like "The Bumpity-Bump," as well as his Columbia-released collections of anniversary, Irish, Christmas, and spiritual numbers. But when he set his mind to it, as he does on *Lost in a Cloud*, he could coax some pretty laid-back sounds out of the old Hammond. Subtitled "Music to Relax By," *Lost in a Cloud* is background music for that contemplative 3 a.m. martini, after all the guests – except, maybe, for one – have ankled the party.

– JW

Bernie **Green**

Ken **Griffin**

Merv **Griffin**

Harry **Grube**

Vince **Guaraldi**

On CD: Modern Music from San Francisco (Original Jazz Classics); Vince Guaraldi Trio (Original Jazz Classics, 1991); Greatest Hits (Fantasy, 1992); A Flower Is a Lovesome Thing (Original Jazz Classics, 1994); Vince Guaraldi in Person (Original Jazz Classics, 1997); The Latin Side of Vince Guaraldi (original Jazz Classics, 1996)

Guitars Unlimited Plus 7

Bobby **Hackett**

As the lonely romantic soloist on a lot of the Jackie Gleason albums, as well as with his work for other orchestras and his records under his own name, Bobby Hackett was probably the king of lounge-music trumpet. Chet Baker was sadder and moodier, but he was also far more self-involved – which, of course, distinguishes real jazz from real lounge music. Hackett always played for the people, choosing pop standards and movie themes and giving them the kind of thoughtfully tasteful treatment that never intruded, and always enhanced.

– JW

On CD: The Memorable & Mellow Bobby Hackett (Project 3, 1993); You Stepped out of a Dream (Pair, 1995); String of Pearls (Pearl, 1996)

Earle **Hagen**

Bobby **Hammack** Quartet

Dave **Harris** and the Powerhouse Five

Jimmie **Haskell** (and His Orchestra)

Jimmie Haskell's name showed up in the '90s – long after his surfin' days of the '60s. Haskell arranged the score for the Richard Dreyfuss film Mr. Holland's Opus *and conducted the orchestra on k.d. lang's ultimate lounge record* Drag.

Sunset Surf .... 25 - 15
   (Capitol ST-1915, 1963)
Teen Love Themes .... 25 - 15
   (Capitol ST-2151, 1964)
Countdown in Stereo .... 25 - 15

Tony **Hatch**
(The Tony Hatch Sound)

In addition to his own uniquely British orchestral imprints, Tony Hatch is known for writing Petula Clark's one big hit, "Downtown."

Downtown With Tony Hatch .... 20 - 12
   (Pye, 1967)
The Tony Hatch Sound .... 20 - 12
Mr. Nice Guy .... 20 - 12

On CD: Hatchback (Sequel, 1998); Best of Tony Hatch and His Orchestra (Sequel, 1997)

Richard **Hayman**

Ruby .... 10 - 6
   (Audio Fidelity AFE-6302, 1981)
Cinematic Sounds .... 10 - 6
   (Command RS-941-SD)
Genuine Electric Latin Love Machine .... 25 - 15
   (Command)
Reminiscing .... 10 - 6
   (Mercury MG-20113)
Love is a Many Splendored Thing .... 10 - 6
   (Mercury MG-20123)
Come With Me to Far-Away Places .... 10 - 6
   (Mercury MG-20129)
Only Memories .... 10 - 6
   (Mercury MG-20248/SR-60100)
Great Motion Picture Themes of Victor Young .... 10 - 6
   (Mercury MG-20369/SR-60012)
Voodoo! .... 25 - 15
   (Mercury MG-20465)
Havana in Hi-Fi .... 10 - 6
   (Mercury SR-60000)

Humorous songster Tom Lehrer isn't necessarily lounge, but a friend of his thought hooking him up with a cocktail kingpin might help Lehrer's musical wit get more recognition. Lehrer's friend, Robert Sylvester, was part owner of a label that had produced some "esoteric classical music" (as described in the liner notes to Lehrer's *Songs and More Songs* on Rhino). Sylvester thought Lehrer could have a hit single if he were backed by orchestra instead of a mere, lone piano. Sylvester brought in **Richard Hayman,** who in 1960 wrote orchestral arrangements for four Lehrer tunes, two of which ("Poisoning Pigeons in the Park" and the notorious "Masochism Tango") were released as a single. Alas, radio was no more receptive to this version of Lehrer's devilish wit.

– TC

Neal Hefti's claim to fame? You've hummed it – or at least dah-nah-nah'ed it – a few times before. He wrote the theme to the cheese-ball *Batman* television series. Hey, even the Who covered it. There's more bat-music on a blam! pow! various artists CD release called *Batmania: Songs Inspired by the Batman TV Series* from Varese Sarabande. Hear Al Hirt play Hefti's famous theme, then have the seltzer nearby when the stars of the series itself – Burgess Meredith, Frank Gorshin, Adam West – take turns singing.

– TC

Harmonica Holiday 10-6
(Mercury PPS-6005)
Let's Get Together.. 10-6
(Mercury-Wing MGW-12100)
Caramba! Exotic Sounds of the Americas........................... 10-6
(Mercury PPS-6010/SR-60103)
Music for a Quiet Evening.. 10-6
(Mercury MG-20048)
Serenade for Love.. 10-6
(Mercury Wing SRW-16239)
Two Tickets to Rome 10-6
(Mercury MG-20235)
Music for People Who Can't Sleep 10-6
(Mercury MG-20184)

On CD: Music for Lonely Lovers (Naxos International, 1990); Viva Espana and Mexico (Naxos International, 1991); Waltzing Cat: The Music of Leroy Anderson (Naxos International); Great Love Stories (Naxos International)

Ernie **Heckscher**

Nostalgia on Nob Hill, Vol. 1... 5-3
(Earl 1700)
Nostalgia on Nob Hill, Vol. 2... 5-3
(Earl 1800)
At the Fabulous Fairmount.. 5-3
(Verve MGV-4020)
Hollywood Hits for Dancing 5-3
(Verve V6-4047)

Neal **Hefti**

Left and Right 20-12
(Columbia CS-8316, 1956)
Swingin' on a Coral Reef 20-12
(Coral CRL-56083, 1953)
Neal Hefti... 20-12
(Coral CRL-5603, 1953)
The Hollywood Song Book... 20-12
(Coral CRL-57241)
The Odd Couple [soundtrack]... 20-12
(Dot DLP-25862)
The Young at Bop 20-12
(Emarcy 26001)

On CD: Neal Hefti (RCA)

Mel **Henke**

On CD: La Dolce Henke (Scamp, 1997)

"... (A)ll of these chart-toppers have one thing in common – captivating melody; and the lushly romantic Hollyridge Strings see to it that every bit of it is excitingly and beautifully preserved ... Rarely does the word sumptuous apply to the 'top 40' ... *The Hollyridge Strings Play Oldies But Goldies* is one rewarding occasion when it most assuredly does!"

[from the liner notes for *The Hollyridge Strings Play Oldies But Goldies*]

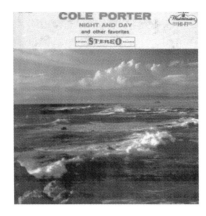

Joel **Herron** and His Orchestra

The Way You Look Tonight .... 5 - 3
and Other Jerome Kern Favorites
(Westminster WST-15002)
Cole Porter: Night and Day .... 5 - 3
and Other Favorites
(Westminster WST-15028)

Al **Hirt**

Raw Sugar/Sweet Sauce/Banana Pudding .... 5 - 3
   (Monument, KZ-32913)
Horn A-Plenty [arranged by Billy May] .... 5 - 3
   (RCA Victor, LPM/LSP-2446, 1962)
Honey in the Horn .... 5 - 3
   (RCA Victor, LPM/LSP-2733, 1965)
Sugar Lips .... 5 - 3
   (RCA Victor, LPM/LSP-2965, 1964)
The Best of Al Hirt .... 5 - 3
   (RCA Victor, LPM/LSP-3309)

On CD: Our Man in New Orleans (Special Music, 1992)

Don **Ho**

The Don Ho Show! .... 5 - 3
   (Reprise R-6161)
You're Gonna Hear From Me .... 5 - 3
   (Reprise R-6219)
Tiny Bubbles .... 5 - 3
   (Reprise RS-6232)

On CD: Greatest Hits (Reprise, 1989)

The **Hollyridge Strings**

The Beatles Song Book .... 20 - 12
   (Capitol T/ST-2116, 1964)
The Beach Boys Song Book .... 15 - 9
   (Capitol T/ST-2156)
Hits Made Famous by the Four Seasons .... 10 - 6
   (Capitol T/ST-2199)
The Beatles Song Book, Vol. 2 .... 20 - 12
   (Capitol T/ST-2202)

On CD: *The Beatles Song Book (Varese Sarabande, 1996)*

Hollywood Studio Orchestra

LeRoy **Holmes**
(and His Orchestra)

"You are the target, the major mark of the New Cinema: the Blitzkrieg Aesthetics of movies Now. They are the wrong ones, the strong ones, the potent children of the new exploration, and their brusque, brash, irreverend (sic), let-it-all-hang-out attitude makes the most rough and ready viewer take a hard look at himself, and the most sensitive and vulnerable hide out altogether, or condemn them all as diabolical and obscene.

"Until very recently, the list of topics they wouldn't discuss, didn't picture, was as long as the arm of the Hays Office, and most films, effectively censored by the Gray Ladies of the Blue Nose Establishment, were little more than fantasies in Candyapple Hogwash. *Andy Hardy* and *Superman* have their place in the universe of film, but not to the exclusion of more real, more valid characterizations. *National Velvet* and *Pillow Talk* are a part of the pageant of movies, but one can strangle on whipped cream perhaps more easily than on vinegar. And so, there has been a reaction, a revolt, against the Tyranny of the Pure …

"In features such as those whose themes are the subject of this album, some of the best of the New Provocative Films, a new kind of exploration is at work. To be provoked is to be activated, to be roused, to be challenged, and film is the electric, the immediate Medium. Provocative Films … right. A powerful combination. Think well or ill of them as you will, they are here …"
[from the P.F. Edwards liner notes for *Themes From the New Provocative Film*]

"Music that soothes, music that invites friendly and intimate conversation in an unhurried atmosphere, music that is charming and gay and harmonically compatible with the better things of life … that's the mood the Hollywood Studio Orchestra designs so smartly in this album of preferred dinner music … You'll recognize the exotic flavor of Kashmiri Song, and the continental touch of Valse Triste … the nostalgia of Londonderry Air … the wistfulness of None But the Lonely Heart … and other ever-popular melodies that have stood the test of time as only distinctive, melodious music can … Capitol is privileged to present Music By Candlelight … May it help bring you, too, the better things of life."

[from the liner notes for *Music by Candlelight*]

Released well past lounge-music's prime, *Themes From the New Provocative Films* nonetheless captures the spirit – musical as well as carnal – of lounge's randier side. From the – yes – provocative cover photo (worth the price of admission) to the selections, including themes from such bona fide skin flicks as *All the Loving Couples* and *I, a Lover*, this is a hot one. And the notion that it was also available in eight-track strikes us, for some reason, as amusing.

– JW

Lena **Horne**

On CD: Love Is the Thing (RCA, 1994); Lena Horne Christmas (Razor & Tie, 1995); Lena Horne (Fat Boy, 1995); Stormy Weather (Charly Budget, 1995); Stormy Weather (Prime Cuts, 1995); Lena Sings Hollywood (EMI, 1996); Stormy Lady (Laserlight); Stormy Weather: The Legendary Lena (Bluebird, 1992); Lena Horne at M-G-M (Rhino, 1996); The Best of Lena Horne (Capitol/Curb, 1993); Biography (Capitol, 1998); Lena Goes Latin (Decca, 1991); Like Latin (Decca, 1991); Lena in Hollywood (Capitol, 1996)

Dick **Hyman**
and His Orchestra

Dick Hyman, the man who believed in his heart that popular hits sounded best when played on harpsichord, channeled his considerable compositional talents into film scores later in his life. He wrote the scores for two nostalgic Woody Allen films: The Purple Rose of Cairo *and* Radio Days.

60 Great All Time Songs, Vol. 6 .... 5 - 3
   (MGM E-3588)
Dick Hyman & Harpsichord in Hi Fi... 5 - 3
   (MGM E-3606)
Moon Gas [with Mary Mayo] .... 250 - 150
   (MGM SE-4119)
Birth of Rhapsody in Blue.. 5 - 3
   (Music Masters 60113)
Sensuous Piano of "D" .... 5 - 3
   (Project 3 5054, 1971)

On CD: Moog: The Electric Eclectics of Dick Hyman (Varese, 1997)

Bill **Irwin**

Seduction [produced by Rod McKuen].. 5 - 3
   (HiFi L-1022)

Dick **Jacobs**

[see Electro-Sonic Orchestra, The]

Horst **Jankowski**

The Genius of Jankowski.. 5 - 3
   (Mercury SR-60993, 1965)
More Genius of Jankowski .... 5 - 3
   (Mercury SR-61054, 1965)
Still More Genius of Jankowski .... 5 - 3
   (Mercury SR-61076, 1966)
So, What's New? .... 5 - 3
   (Mercury SR-61093, 1966)
Baby, But Grand! .... 5 - 3
   (Mercury SR-21106)
And We Got Love .... 5 - 3
   (Mercury SR-61160)
Piano Affairs... 5 - 3
   (Mercury SR-61195)
Jankowski Plays Jankowski .... 5 - 3
   (Mercury SR-61219)
Enjoy Jankowski .... 5 - 3
   (Mercury/Wing SRW-16385)
With Love .... 5 - 3
   (Mercury SR-61125)

A Walk in the Evergreens .... 5 - 3
  (Mercury SR-61232)

On CD: Instrumental Gems of the '60s (Collectors Choice, 1995); Instrumentals (Time-Life)

Gordon **Jenkins**

Gordon Jenkins conducted and arranged on dozens of Sinatra records. He showed up on a delightful though obscure project in 1996, writing the string arrangements for the album Marshmallows *by an overly mellow New York City modern rock band called the For Carnation.*

Manhattan Tower .... 5 - 3
  (Capitol W-766, 1956)
Manhattan Tower [reissue] .... 5 - 3
  (Decca 78011)
Time to Dance With Gordon Jenkins .... 5 - 3
  (Capitol CCF-2641, 1951)
Hawaiian Wedding Song .... 5 - 3
  (Columbia CS-8564)
The Magic World of Gordon Jenkins .... 5 - 3
  (Columbia CL-1882/CS-8682)
Seven Dreams .... 5 - 3
  (Decca 79011)
Blue Prelude .... 5 - 3
  (Sunset 1149)
Dreamer's Holiday .... 5 - 3
  (Vocalion 3615)
Sophisticated .... 5 - 3
  (1969)

On CD: Sophisticated (Pair); Collection (Razor and Tie, 1997)

Henry **Jerome**

Brazen Brass Goes Hollywood .... 5 - 3
  (Decca DL-4085)
Brazen Brass Plays Songs Everybody Knows .... 5 - 3
  (Decca DL-4106)
Brazen Brass Brings Back the Bands .... 5 - 3
  (Decca DL-4125)
Brazen Brass Features Saxes .... 5 - 3
  (Decca DL-4127)
Brazen Brass Zings the Strings .... 5 - 3
  (Decca DL-4187)

Jonathan and Darlene

Jack Jones

Jack Jones won the Grammy for Best Performance by a Male Singer in 1962 for his record "Lollipops and Roses."

Singer Jo Stafford and Paul Weston were married not long after Weston started arranging and conducting Stafford's records. They shared a quirky sense of humor which they decided to spring on the public after a bit of a dare. Weston was playing piano at a party one night, tinkering around and playing purposely badly. Stafford joined in, singing purposely off-key, and the laughter was raucous all around. Some label reps from Columbia, however, told them they should record the act. They did, and Jonathan and Darlene were born. These albums of fumbling piano and off-key singing were a bit of a hit, and *Jonathan and Darlene in Paris* even won a Grammy award for Best Comedy Recording. Tough to listen to sometimes, but evocative of the party's noodling drunk at the piano.

– TC

Bert Kaempfert and his Orchestra were No. 1 for 3 weeks in 1960 with *Wonderland by Night* and also had hits with "Tenderly" (No. 31 in '61), "Red Roses for a Blue Lady" (No. 11 in '65) and "Three O'Clock in the Morning" (No. 33 in '65). All instrumentals, of course.

– JW

"Remember when you first heard the Bert Kaempfert sound? Perhaps it was one of his earlier hits … 'Danke Schoen' or 'Wonderland by Night'; and suddenly you were aware of music that reached out and grabbed hold of you – a lead trumpet that soared to dramatic heights … a sense of tempo that invited you to dance or listen with equal appeal. That's when you probably said, 'Love that Bert Kaempfert' – and joined a fan club of millions in every corner of the world."

[from the liner notes for … *Love That Bert Kaempfert*]

On CD: Impossible Dream (MCA Special Products, 1995); Mood Is Love (Quicksilver, 1993); Christmas (LaserLight, 1994); New Jack Swing (Linn, 1997); Greatest Hits (Capitol-Curb, 1990); Greatest Hits (MCA, 1995)

Irving **Joseph**

Bert **Kaempfert**

Although Germany's Kaempfert was best-known for songs that featured a lonely-sounding trumpet soaring above lush orchestral arrangements, he was not the trumpeter on his records. Composer-conductor-arranger Kaempfert played clarinet, saxophone, piano and accordian, but no trumpet. (Charly Tabor was the guy on 'Wonderland by Night,' Kaempfert's biggest hit.)

One calm spring night, having wined

and dined, having wandered to the

terrace of his apartment from which

point the city of London seems to

rest easily on a bed of soft lights

and sounds, and having found in the

air a slight fragrance of jasmine and

a touch of romance, a man closed

his eyes and dreamed of Woman:

incessantly captivating, eternal,

without beginning or end, unspeak-

ably beautiful. And she came to him

twelve times, and each time she was

changed, each time she appeared

she wore a new face, a new dress, a

new personality; but he loved her

each time she came to him: he loved

her when she appeared personified

as "temptation," with dark eyes

flashing and bright red lips bent on

passion, committed to sensual

provocation, destined to rule by

desire and ruin by annulment; ... and

of Chloe, what of Chloe? Lost, never

to be found? What of Chloe? Do we

On CD: That Happy Feeling (Taragon, 1996); Christmas in Wonderland (Taragon, 1996); Three O'Clock in the Morning (Taragon, 1997); The Magic Music of Far Away Places (Taragon, 1997); Red Roses (Alex, 1993); The Best of Bert Kaempfert (Mobile Fidelity, 1994); The Very Best of Bert Kaempfert (Taragon, 1997); That Latin Feeling/Blue Midnight (Taragon, 1997)

Anton **Karas**

On CD: Anton Karas (Victor [Japan])

Johnny **Keating**

Anita **Kerr**
(The Anita Kerr Singers)

[see also The San Sebastian Strings]

Shut off that old transistor, mister, Anita's in another world. Purge thy soul of ching-ching-a-ching-ching. Concentrate on taking one lovely musical line and turning it into one classic-all-time-championship-top-ten-doodle. DoodDdDdle went her arrangements ... arrangements that would be almost heretical in the revved up Hollywood-hip studios where she was to record. (Violinists, gazing over the charts, would weep – "Glissandos, Herbie, glissandos!") (And there was to be one frightened looking sideman, shoved to one corner, sitting at – can it be?? – a harpsichord!)

   [from the liner notes for *Slightly Baroque*]

On CD: Music Is Her Name (Columbia, 1992); Favorites (Bainbridge, 1994)

weep or do we laugh and turn away? ... and Jezebel, the temptress, her beauty matched only by her thirst and passion for evil–and he watched her. And, as with all the others, he felt he knew them: they moved him and they tempted him–all of them, all twelve. The man came out of his reverie to put it down on paper, to breathe into the music the character essence of each siren, to make them live in the music as they had lived in his dream.

That's when John Keating created this special and superb LP.

[from the liner notes for *Temptation*]

Pete **King**
(Orchestra and Chorale)

Wayne **King**

"What is mood music? Is it simply music that puts you in a mood? … Not quite! A mood, according to Mr. Webster of dictionary fame, is 'a state of mind.' The 'mood' in mood music, however, is easy to listen to but hard to define. We're going to take the easier, and by far the more pleasant way out, and let Wayne King and his orchestra do the explaining for us …"

[from the liner notes for *Wayne King in Hi-Fi*]

On CD: Best of Wayne King (MCA); Golden Favorites (MCA, 1994)

Gershon **Kingsley**

[See also Perrey and Kingsley]

Eartha **Kitt**

On CD: In Person at the Plaza (GNP); Songs (RCA, 1990); Sentimental Eartha (See for Miles, 1995); That Seductive Eartha (Camden, 1996); Back in Business (Decca); Miss Kitt to You (RCA, 1992); The Best of Eartha Kitt (Import, 1994); Eartha Quake [five-CD boxed set] (Bear Family, 1994); The Best of Eartha Kitt: Where Is My Man? (Hot Production, 1995)

Thurston **Knudson**

Jimmie **Komack**

Andre **Kostelanetz**

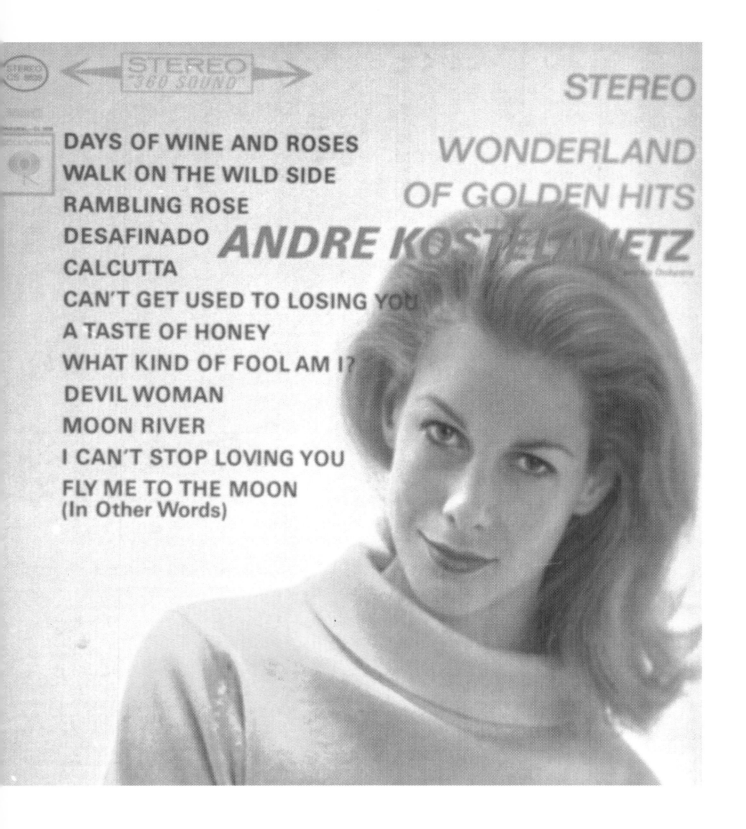

"Andre Kostelanetz is a demonstrative
commentator on all things musical in
this day and age. He lends a constant
ear to the sounds and styles that rise up
around us, embraces the inventions and
expansions of adventuring creators,
selects the melodies that impress him
the most, then offers up his translations
with, in the words of T.S. Eliot, 'simple
force and subtle variation.' His is a
habit-forming art that has brightened
the classics and contemporary fare.
Look at the repertoire here. The pieces
segue from lush movie themes to 'pop'
chart hits to ethereal imaginations to
psychological drama to scenic descrip-
tions to serious compositions. The
Maestro treats each without disturbing
musical tricks and impractical circus
stunts. He adds special flavor and dec-
oration and choreography of movement
that emerge into enticing shapes and
forms. The side effects are simple pleasures … "

[from the liner notes for *You Light
Up My Life*]

Kostelanetz in Wonderland: .... 5 - 3
Stereo Wonderland of Golden Hits
   (Columbia CS-8839)
Golden Encores .... 5 - 3
   (Columbia CS-8878/CL-2078)
You Light Up My Life .... 5 - 3
   (Columbia JC-35328, 1978)
Eight All-Time Hits [7-inch LP] .... 5 - 3
   (Columbia ML-2106)
For the Young at Heart .... 5 - 3
   (Columbia)
For the Young at Heart [reissue] .... 5 - 3
   (Columbia Ltd. Ed. LE-10068)

On CD: Carmen Without Words (Sony, 1990); Greatest Movie Hits (Sony Special Products, 1995); Christmas Concert (Sony Special Products, 1995); Moon River (Sony Special Products, 1995); 16 Most Requested Songs (Sony Special Products, 1991)

Francis **Lai**

Francis Lai Performs .... 5 - 3
   (Decca MRS-508)
Love Is a Funny Thing .... 5 - 3
   (MCA MCA-25111)
Love Story [soundtrack] .... 5 - 3
   (MCA 27017, 1980)
A Man and a Woman [Un homme et une femme] [soundtrack] .... 5 - 3
   (United Artists UAL-4147/UAS-5147, 1966)
A Man And A Woman [soundtrack] .... 5 - 3
   (Liberty LN-10275, 1985)
Vivre pour vivre [Live for Life] [soundtrack] .... 5 - 3
   (United Artists, 1967)

On CD: A Man and a Woman/Live for Life [soundtracks] (Decca); Bandes Originales des Films de Claude Lelouch (Musidisc, 1996); The Very Best of Francis Lai (Skyline)

Duncan **Lamont**

The Best of the Bossa Novas .... 5 - 3
   (MFP, 1970)

The **Latin Soul Brothers**

[see Pucho and the Latin Soul Brothers]

Steve **Lawrence**

On CD: The Very Best of Steve Lawrence (Taragon, 1995)

Steve **Lawrence**
and Eydie Gormé

On CD: We Got Us/Steve and Eydie Sing the Golden Hits (Jasmine, 1996); Steve and Eydie Sing the Golden hits (MCA Special Products); We'll Take Romance: The Best of Steve and Eydie (Musicrama, 1995); Best of Steve Lawrence and Eydie Gormé (Music Club, 1998)

Eddie **Layton**

Katie **Lee**

Pop psychology saw its heyday in the '50s. What with everyone starting to think too much about themselves, the hipsters of the day did their best to skewer the phenomenon. After all, who wants an audience full of people dwelling on their neuroses? Katie Lee, a rugged cowpoke from Colorado, used her brief few minutes in the limelight to burst the bubble of pop psychology, offering up an entire album of songs over-analyzing analysis. Songs of Couch and Consultation, *recorded with Bob Thompson, features an intriguing list of titles – "I Can't Get Adjusted to the You Who Got Adjusted to Me," "Shrinker Man," "Hush Little Sibling," "Repressed Hostility Blues," "The Will to Fail," "Stay as Sick as You Are" – but remember, sometimes a cigar is just a cigar.*
– TC

Peggy **Lee**

Peg of my heart

The lovely Peggy Lee.

Rhino Records

Jazz pianist Ramsey Lewis had been kicking around with his trio since early '56, when he signed up with the Chicago-based Argo Records for his first LP, *Ramsey Lewis and His Gentlemen of Swing.* Eight years later, the trio dented the pop and R&B charts with a tune called "Something You Got" – a single that foreshadowed their enormous success the next year with instrumental versions of the pop hits "The 'In' Crowd," "Hang On, Sloopy," and "A Hard Day's Night." Lewis has continued to craft his easy-swinging, intelligent piano-based jazz ever since.

– JW

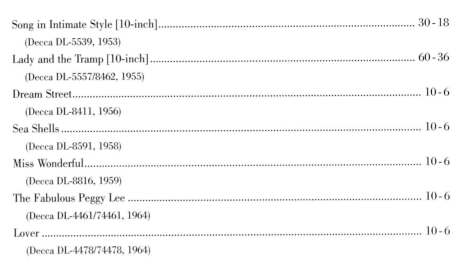

On CD: Seduction (Pair, 1989); I've Got a Crush On You (Avid, 1995); Sings for You (Avid, 1995); Christmas (Empire, 1997); The Best of the Decca Years (MCA, 1997); All-Time Greatest Hits (Curb, 1990); The Best of Peggy Lee (Decca, 1992); Fever & Other Hits (CEMA, 1992); Classics (Capitol/Curb, 1993); Spotlight on Peggy Lee (Capitol, 1995); More of the Best (Delta, 1996); Some of the Best (Delta, 1996); Things Are Swingin'/Jump for Joy (Capitol, 1997); Extra Special!/Somethin' Groovy! (EMI, 1998); Fever (Golden Sounds , 1998); The Peggy Lee Songbook (Music Masters); Black Coffee (MCA, 1994); Best of the Decca Years (MCA, 1997); Black Coffee and Other Delights (Decca, 1994); Christmas Carousel (Capitol, 1990); Beauty and the Beat (Capitol, 1992)

Les Cinq Modernes

Ramsey **Lewis**

Liberace

On CD: Love Letters (MCA Special Products, 1990); As Time Goes By (MCA Special Products, 1995); All the Things You Are (Essex, 1994); Christmas Through the Years (Delta, 1996); Christmas at Liberace's (AVI, 1996); 'Twas the Night Before Christmas (Special Music); Christmas (MCA Special Products, 1995); Here's Liberace (MCA, 1987); The Best of Liberace (USA Music Group, 1994); The Best of Liberace (MCA); Liberace's Greatest Hits (Columbia); Most Requested Songs (Columbia, 1990); The Golden Age of Television, Vol. 1 (Curb, 1991); Collection (Castle, 1993); By Request (Pair, 1993); Liberace/Pick of Liberace (Sony Special Products, 1995); Unplugged (Foundation, 1995); Plays the Classics (Music Club, 1998); Lounging With Lee (Hip-O, 1998)

Enoch **Light**

On CD: Persuasive Percussion: Bachelor Pad Music (Varese Sarabande, 1995); Provocative Percussion: Bachelor Pad Music (Varese Sarabande); The Greatest Big Band Themes of All Time (Project 3, 1995); Spanish Strings (Project 3); The Most Beautiful Music in the World (Project 3)

Living Brass

Julie **London**

One in the infinite string of Living Brass, Living Strings, Living Voices, etc. LPs from Camden, RCA's budget label, *Living Brass Plays A Henry Mancini Tribute* leans fairly heavily on covers of songs from the then-current movie, *Gunn*, Blake Edwards' big-screen reworking of his seminal lounge TV series, *Peter Gunn.* The album, for instance, begins with Gunn's "Bye Bye," the famed "Peter Gunn Theme" wedded to lyrics by Jay Livingston and Ray Evans. (Sample: "Every night your line is busy/All that buzzin' makes me dizzy/ Couldn't count on all my fingers/All the dates you've had with swingers.")

– JW

Claudine Longet was a whispery French chanteuse and former show-girl who unfortunately became most famous not for her great (if some-times near-inaudible) vocal treat-ments of pop hits like "Hello, Hello" and "Here, There and Everywhere," but for offing pro skier Vladimir "Spider" Sabich with a .22 pistol. The former wife of Andy Williams – and mother of his three children – she was living with Sabich when the accident occurred. Convicted of criminally negligent manslaughter, she served 30 days in jail in early 1977 and then faded out of the public eye.

"Because of the many cards and letters I've received, the prayers, I feel very good about everybody," she told an Associated Press reporter on the day of the sentenc-ing. "People are very warm and sensitive. I realized that people are very beautiful."

– JW

On CD: Julie London Sings Cole Porter (Capitol, 1991); Julie Is Her Name, Vols. 1 and 2 (EMI, 1992); Cry Me a River (CEMA); Time for Love: The Best of Julie London (Rhino, 1990); Calendar Girl/Your Number Please (EMI, 1997); Cry Me a River (Glden Sounds, 1998); Julie London at Home (EMI, 1997); Around Midnight (EMI, 1997)

Claudine **Longet**

Vincent **Lopez**

Mundell **Lowe**

As legendary cheap-film auteur Roger Corman has shown us, you can do a lot of subversive things in a low-budget picture. His nurse and cheerleader pictures of the '70s, for instance, were full of all sorts of social-liberal agitprop, which patrons thought was fine as long as someone peeled off her top every half-hour or so.

Guitarist-composer Mundell Lowe did something of the same sort with his score for the $70,000 exploitation film *Satan in High Heels*, putting together a first-class group of moody jazz tunes (with titles like "From Mundy On" and "Blues for a Stripper") and a terrific group to play them (including future *Tonight Show* heavyweights like Doc – then "Carl" – Severinsen and Clark Terry on trumpets and Ed Shaughnessy on drums. Clearly, he was trying for something other than a standard skin-flick soundtrack. He was doing that most admirable of artistic endeavors: trying to create something a little bit better than it needed to be. With his 10 tunes for *Satan in High Heels*, he succeeded.
– JW

"… I think I have recorded about 10 or 12 other albums of my own, and this is the first time I can say I was really pleased.

"George Duvivier, my friend, and probably the world's greatest bass player today, obviously felt the same way, because as we got into his car for the trip home, he turned to me and said, '"Old buddy – this album is gonna shake a lot of people up.' I knew he was serious and I hoped what he was saying would happen."

[from Mundell Lowe's liner notes for *Satan in High Heels*]

Arthur **Lyman**

In his many personal appearances, the romantic and personable Lyman has had particular appeal for feminine listeners of all ages. This charm is a sort of personal magnetism accented by a movie idol appearance, but without any particular intent, and unaccompanied by the twisting and carrying on of the many popular purposeful charmers. Obviously Arthur Lyman gets through to girls young and old; in fact to everyone, with much natural personal appeal and sensual sounds.

[from the liner notes for *I Wish You Love*]

On CD: *Music for a Bachelor's Den, Vol. 5: The Best of the Arthur Lyman Group (DCC); Music for a Bachelor's Den, Vol. 6: More of the Best of the Arthur Lyman Group (DCC); Taboo (DCC); Taboo (Rykodisc, 1996); Taboo, Vol. 2: New Exotic Sounds of Arthur Lyman (Rykodisc, 1998); Sonic Sixties (Tradition, 1996); The Exotic Sound of Arthur Lyman (Surfside, 1995); Pearly Shells (GNP Crescendo, 1989); Exotic Sounds (Legacy, 1995); Hawaiian Sunset (Rykodisc, 1996); With a Christmas Vibe (Rykodisc, 1996); Leis of Jazz: Jazz Sounds of Arhut Lyman (Rykodisc, 1998); Taboo/Yellow Bird (DCC); Music of Hawaii (Columbia-Legacy); Best of the Arthur Lyman Group (DCC, 1996); More of the Best of the Arthur Lyman Group (DCC, 1996)*

Machito

Afro Cuban Jazz .... 250 - 150
   (Verve VE-2522, 1949)
Afro Cuban Jazz [reissue] .... 100 - 60
   (Clef MGC0689, 1956)
Mambo Inn, Sambia, Yo Tengo un Mate .... 75 - 45
   (Columbia, 1952)
World's Greatest Latin Band .... 60 - 36
   (Crescendo GNPS-72, 1961)
Machito's Afro Cuban [10-inch] .... 125 - 75
   (Decca DL-5157, 1950)
Irving Berlin in Latin America .... 25 - 15
   (Forum SF-9040)
Mambo Holiday .... 25 - 15
   (Harmony HL-7040)
Jungle Drums [10-inch] .... 125 - 75
   (Mercury MG-25009, 1950)
Kenya .... 50 - 30
   (Roulette 52006, 1957)
Machito With Flute to Boot [with Herbie Mann] .... 60 - 36
   (Roulette R-52026, 1959)
Mambo Sentimental .... 75 - 45
   (Seeco, 1952)
Mambo America .... 100 - 60
   (Tico, 1954)
El As de la Rumba .... 100 - 60
   (Tico, 1958)
Feeding the Chickens, Consternacion .... 100 - 60
   (1952)

On CD: *Mucho Macho: Machito and His Afro-Cuban Salseros (Pablo, 1991); Machito! (Top Ten Hits, 1991); Machito and His Afro Cuban Jazz Ensemble (Fania, 1993); Mambo in Jazz (Saludos Amigos, 1993); Tea for Two (Saludos Amigos, 1993); Yo Soy La Rumba (Polygram, 1994); Machito Mucho (Charly, 1995); Dance Date (Palladium, 1995); Mucho Mucho Machito*

(Palladium, 1995); Machito and His Afro Cubans (Fantasy, 1995); This Is Machito (Polygram, 1995); Afro Cuban Grooves (Delta, 1996); Machito and His Afro Cubans (Harlequin, 1996); Afro Cuban Jazz (International, 1997)

José **Maderia**
(and His Orchestra)

Havana … 2 a.m. [with Carlos Montoya].. 5 - 3
  (Masterseal MSLP-5003, 1957)

Michel **Magne**

Voices of Exotica and Percussion.. 250 - 150
  (Columbia) [called "the best exotica LP ever!" by *Forever Lounge* price consultant Gary Johnson]

Joe **Maize**
(and His Cordsmen)

Presenting Joe Maize and His Cordsmen.. 10 - 6
  (Decca DL-8590, 1958)
Hawaiian Dreams .... 10 - 6
  (Decca DL-8817, 1959)
Isle of Dreams.. 10 - 6
  (Decca DL-4555/74555, 1965)

Richard **Maltby**

Swingin' Down the Lane .... 5 - 3
  (Columbia CS-8083)
Hello, Young Lovers .... 5 - 3
  (Columbia CS-8151, 1959)
Music From Mr. Lucky .... 5 - 3
  (RCA Camden CAL-600)
Just a Minute!... 5 - 3
  (Sesac PA-201/202)
Hue-Fi Moods by Maltby... 5 - 3
  (Vik LX-1051)
Manhattan Bandstand.. 5 - 3
  (Vik LX-1068)

Henry **Mancini**

"… 'Lucky' is a true cosmopolite. He's been everywhere, seen and done just about everything and knows everybody. He has a suave, sophisticated, polished and international demenaor. His adventures may involve anyone from a Bowery bum to a deposed king. He's a mystery man,

Something of an oddity, the budget-label offering *Havana … 2 a.m.* features half laid-back cha-cha from Madeira's group (Side A), and half solo flamenco guitar (Side B) from Montoya, the masterful Spanish gypsy. And yes, Montoya's selections include "Maleguena," which is to flamenco guitarists what "Orange Blossom Special" is to Branson music theaters.

– JW

There are lots of places to start a lounge-music collection, but for our money there's no better one that with Mancini's groundbreaking scores for *Peter Gunn* , the television show that brought the ultrahip lounge culture to Middle America. Between grim tussles with no-nonsense hoods, the sharkshin-suited Gunn (played by Craig Stevens) hung out at a jazz lounge called Mother's, where his paramour Edie (Lola Albright) purred lyrics into a microphone, in front of the coolest club band in the world.

Mancini and Ms. Albright ultimately teamed up for what may be the best female-vocal lounge LP ever recorded, *Dreamsville* (see Lola Albright entry). Taken together, the two Gunn discs and Ms. Albright's *Dreamsville* are just about too much, with enough quavery vibraphone and whispery vocalizing to launch the liquor-augmented listener into a starry void somewhere beyond Jupiter.

– JW

intriguing to women, admired and envied by men.

"Mancini's ambitious assignment was to project. musically, Lucky's involved personality along wtih those of his amusing sidekick, Andamo, and Lucky's beautiful girl friends. Since we were fully aware of Mancini's creative talent, we were not at all surprised when he again delivered exactly what we wanted. We also knew, from experience, that this excellent music would continue week after week …

"So this album is Mr. Lucky and it is good music. In addition, it is Henry Mancini. That, in itself, is sufficient recommendation for me."

[from Blake Edwards' liner notes for *Music From 'Mr. Lucky'*]

"If modern jazz becomes indelibly linked with manslaughter, murder, mayhem, wise-cracking private eyes and droll policemen, the brunt of the responsibility must be borne by composer **Henry Mancini**. Because of him the point is rapidly being reached where no self-respecting killer would consider pulling the trigger without a sutable jazz background …

"With all this excitement, it was inevitable that others should follow Mancini's lead. TV detectives now swash, buckle and make love to the strains of modern jazz. Mancini feels that the whole thing is leading the public toward an ever greater acceptance of jazz as an art form, benefiting the listener and the musician. Never before have so many people been actively aware of modern jazz. This form of music has found a new medium of exposure …"

[from Bill Olofson's liner notes for *More Music From Peter Gunn*]

In 1967, some seven years after the last new episode of TV's *Peter Gunn* unspooled, series creator Blake Edwards directed and co-wrote (with William Peter Blatty) a new adventure of the slick private dick, this time for the big screen. Not a runaway success (and without Lola Albright), the picture at least featured a new batch of lounge-jazz from *Peter Gunn's* original scorer, Henry Mancini, including a couple of re-interpretations of the show's original hit hit theme.

– JW

More Music From Peter Gunn, more cool vibraphone-flavored TV jazz from the guy who started it all. Some great titles here, too, including "Goofin' at the Coffee House," "A Quiet Gass" and "My Man Shelly" – the latter named, of course, after the great jazz drummer who played on these sessions.

– JW

On CD: Peter Gunn (LaserLight); Mancini Plays Mancini & Other (Special Music, 1987); The Revenge of the Pink Panther (EMI America, 1988); Pure Gold (RCA, 1988); Mancini's "Monster" Hits (Atlantic, 1990); Cinema Italiano: Music of Ennio Morricone (RCA, 1990); Mancini in Surround: Mostly Monsters (RCA, 1990); Glow in the Dark (RCA, 1990); A Legendary Performer (RCA, 1992); Top Hat: Music from the Films of Astaire & ... (RCA, 1992); Love Story (Pair, 1992); As Time Goes By (RCA Victor, 1992); Mancini in Hollywood (RCA, 1993); Moon River (RCA, 1993); Mr. Lucky (RCA, 1993); Son of the Pink Panther (Milan, 1993); The Blues and the Beat (RCA, 1995); Days of Wine and Roses (RCA, 1995); The Mancini Touch (RCA, 1996); Romantic Movie Themes (RCA, 1996); The Second Time Around (Essex, 1996); Movie Memories (Highgrade); Mr. Lucky [soundtrack] (RCA); Instrumental Favorites (Time-Life); In the Pink (RCA); Mancini Magic (Pair); Music from the Films of Blake Edwards (RCA); The Pink Panther [soundtrack] (RCA); Themes from Classic Science Fiction (Varese Sarabande); The Long Hot Summer (MCA); The Pink Panther, Baby Elephant Walk & Other ... (RCA, 1987); Academy Award Collection (Pair, 1988); All-Time Greatest Hits, Vol. 1 (RCA, 1988); Moon River, The Pink Panther & Other Hits (RCA, 1989); As Time Goes By &

Other Classic Movie Love Themes (RCA, 1991); The Music of Henry Mancini (Columbia-Legacy, 1994); In the Pink: The Ultimate Collection (RCA, 1996); The Music of Henry Mancini (Showtunes, 1996); Martinis with Mancini (RCA, 1997); Greatest Hits (Highgrade); Greatest Hits/Pink Panther (Telarc); The Best of Henry Mancini, Vol. 3 (RCA); Collection (Pair); Monster Hits (RCA); Touch of Evil [soundtrack] (Varese Sarabande, 1993); Henry Mancini Christmas (RCA, 1997); The Trail of the Pink Panther (and Other Pink Panther Films) (EMI/Liberty); The Best of Mancini (RCA)

Herbie **Mann**

Common Ground .... 25 - 15
   (Atlantic SD-1343, 1961)
Family of Mann .... 25 - 15
   (Atlantic SD-1371, 1961)
Right Now .... 25 - 15
   (Atlantic SD-1384, 1962)
Do the Bossa Nova with Herbie Mann .... 25 - 15
   (Atlantic SD-1397, 1962)
Latin Fever .... 25 - 15
   (Atlantic SD-1422, 1964)
My Kinda Groove .... 25 - 15
   (Atlantic SD-1433, 1964)
Today! .... 25 - 15
   (Atlantic SD-1454, 1966)
Our Mann Flute .... 25 - 15
   (Atlantic SD-1464, 1966)
The Beat Goes on .... 25 - 15
   (Atlantic SD-1483, 1967)
String Album .... 25 - 15
   (Atlantic SD-1490, 1967)
The Best of Herbie Mann .... 10 - 6
   (Atlantic SD-1544, 1969)
The Mann with the Most .... 40 - 24
   (Bethlehem BCP-6020, 1955)
The Mann with the Most [reissue] .... 5 - 3
   (Bethlehem BCP-6020, 1977)
Latin Mann .... 10 - 6
   (Columbia CL-2388/CS-9188, 1965)
Californians .... 40 - 24
   (Jazzland JLP-95, 1960)
Hi Flutin' .... 50 - 30
   (Mode 114, 1957)
Hi-Flutin' [reissue] .... 5 - 3
   (Premier PS-2001)

Like other cool-jazz icons, Herbie Mann played music that can be problematic when it comes to classifying it as lounge. But Mann – like Chet Baker, Dave Brubeck and even Ramsey Lewis, who came along later – was a popular artist at least as much as he was a hard-core jazzer, and on many of his discs, his flute-driven pieces evoke a kind of beatnik romanticism that's as much coffeehouse as lounge, and equally sweet to hear in the glow of caffeine or gin.

– JW

> " ... 'If there were stars in the eyes of 10,000 persons last night,' wrote a Canadian critic, 'blame it on Mantovani, who appears to have a touch of magic at the end of his slender baton.' No conductor has become so linked with the music his orchestra crates. The soaring, tumbling violins are the most individual feature of Mantovani's scoring ...
>
> "Normally, Mantovani uses twenty-eight strings (six first violins, six second violins, six third violins, four violas, four 'cellos and two double-basses) balanced against thirteen brass, woodwind and percussion. When he is asked about his method of scoring, he replies very simply: 'I hear the music for the full orchestra quite plainly in my head. I simply put it on paper.' That sober statement is typical of his musicianly approach. The real answer to the question of how Mantovani creates his sparkling, luminous orchestrations lies within his imagination ..."
>
> [from Charles Fox's liner notes for *Gems Forever*]

On CD: Best of Herbie Mann (Atlantic); Evolution of Mann: The Herbie Mann Anthology (Rhino, 1995); Sultry Serenade (Original Jazz Classics, 1997); Hi Flutin' (Drive Archive)

Mantovani

On CD: Incomparable Mantovani (LaserLight, 1988; Delta, 1990/1993); Mantovani's Golden Hits (PolyGram, 1990; Intercontinental, 1996); The Mantovani Touch (PolyGram); Mantovani … Memories (PolyGram)

Muzzy **Marcellino**

Richard **Marino**
(Richard Marino Orchestra)

The **Markko Polo** Adventurers

Jack **Marshall**

Dean **Martin**

Dino

The silky smooth Dean Martin.

Rhino Records

"... Swingin', of course, is really Dean's specialty. Because his casual, carefree style falls right in with the rhythmic way of doing a song. And here Nelson Riddle's great orchestra falls wonderfully right in behind Dean, with arrangements that couldn't be more sympathetic if Nelson and spent half a lifetime writing them, after spending another half listening to Dean sing ..."

[from the liner notes for *This Time I'm Swingin'*]

Austria-born Ray Martin was the guy who came off the bench often for RCA's budget label, RCA Camden. He could always be counted on for interesting musical ideas, some straying more toward jazz (see *'Thunderball' and Other Thriller Music*), others toward easy-listening. In *Michelle Going for Baroque,* he takes a program of mostly hip pop tunes ("Yesterday," "As Tears Go By," "What Now My Love"), along with a couple of originals, and recasts them with strings and harpsichord added to the wailing saxes and hip guitars. The result is a slice of offbeat, gimmicky mood-music that holds up awfully well under repeated listenings.

– JW

On CD: Swingin' Down Yonder (Capitol, 1991); Winter Romance (Capitol, 1989); Season's Greetings (CEMA, 1992); I Wish You Love (Great Hits, 1996); Little Old Wine Drinker (DJ Specialist, 1996); Memories Are Made of This [boxed set] (Bear Family, 1997); Happy Hour With Dean Martin (Pair); Sings Italian Favorites (Capitol, 1995); You're Nobody Till Somebody Loves You (Capitol, 1995); Best of Dean Martin (Capitol); Capitol Collectors Series (Capitol, 1989); Best of Dean Martin (Capitol, 1990); All-Time Greatest Hits (Curb, 1991); 24 Golden Hits (Huub, 1991); Greatest Hits (Capitol, 1992); Collection (Castle, 1992); The Great Dean Martin (Goldies, 1993); The Great Dean Martin, Vol. 2 (Goldies, 1995); Spotlight on Dean Martin (Capitol, 1995); Merry Christmas From Dean Martin (Capitol, 1995); That's Amore: The Best of Dean Martin (Capitol, 1996); The Best of Dean Martin: 1962-1968 (Charly, 1996); Capitol Years [two discs] (Capitol, 1996); That's Amore (Ariola Express, 1997); The Best of Dean Martin (Capitol, 1997); Love Songs by Dean Martin (Ranwood, 1997); Return to Me [8-disc boxed set] (Bear Family, 1998); Greatest Hits (Capitol, 1998); Solid Gold (Madacy, 1995)

Freddy **Martin**

Ray **Martin**

"*If you have a sense of musical adventure about you … if you are one of those who swears the world of melodic sound is crashing all around you … if you are of a mind that the salvation for the sound of the '70s (the 1970s) should be steeped in the swing of the 1670s … pull on your boots and straddles. It's time to enjoy yourself going for Baroque … Going for Baroque is, in a sense, rocking Bach. It's a gambol … it's a romp … it's super souped-up musical adventure. It's a sound that may have been almost 300 years ahead of its time. But it's here now. If you like your music properly polished, join Ray Martin going for Baroque. You'll go first-class.*"

[from the Mort Goode liner notes for *Michelle Going for Baroque*]

Skip **Martin**

Mat **Mathews**

On CD: Meditation (Jazz World, 1995)

Johnny **Mathis**

Johnny be good

Mr. Johnny Mathis.

Rhino Records

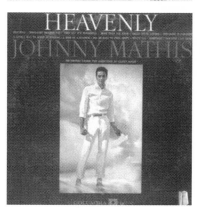

On CD: Celebration: Anniversary Album (Columbia, 1995); All About Love (Columbia, 1996); It's Not for Me to Say (Columbia); Simple (Columbia); 16 Most Requested Songs (Columbia, 1989); The Christmas Music of Johnny Mathis (Columbia, 1993); Collection (Castle, 1993); The Essence of Johnny Mathis (Columbia, 1994); A Personal Collection (Columbia, 1995); Heavenly/Greatest Hits/Live (Sony, 1995); Johnny Mathis 40th Anniversary Edition [boxed set] (Columbia-Legacy, 1996); Wonderful (Sony Special Products, 1996); The Ultimate Hits Collection (Sony, 1998); Heavenly (Columbia); Merry Christmas (Columbia); Open Fire, Two Guitars (Columbia, 1995); I'll Buy You a Star (Columbia, 1996); Johnny (Sony, 1996); More Johnny's Greatest Hits (Columbia); Johnny's Greatest Hits (Columbia)

Robert **Maxwell**
His Harp and His Orchestra

Robert Maxwell, who took the trouble to bill his instrument along with himself, had a No. 15 hit in 1964 with "Shangri-La."

Anytime! 10-6
    (Command RS-913-SD)
Harpistry in Motion 10-6
    (Command RS-932-SD)
A Crowning Performance 10-6
    (Command RS-SD-972-2)
Harpist's Holiday 10-6
    (Harmony HL-7007)
Bewitched 10-6
    (Decca DL-4421)
Shangri-La [reissue of Bewitched] 10-6
    (Decca DL-4421/74421, 1964)
Peg o' My Heart 10-6
    (Decca DL-4563/74563, 1964)
A Song for All Seasons 10-6
[also released as *The Magic of Robert Maxwell*]
    (Decca DL-4609/74609)
Let's Get Away From It All 10-6
    (Decca DL-4723/74723)
Harp in Hi-Fi 10-6
    (Mercury MG-20138)
Harp Magic 10-6
    (MGM E-3171)
The Lamp Is Low 10-6
    (MGM E-3308)
Hi-Fi Harp 10-6
    (MGM E-3360, 1956)
Zing! Went the Strings of My Harp 10-6
    (MGM E-3486)
Music to Make You Starry-Eyed 10-6
    (MGM E-3571)
Red Hot Harp 10-6
    (MGM E-3676)
The Very Best of Robert Maxwell 10-6
    (MGM E-4246)
Spectacular Harps 10-6
    (MGM E-3836, 1957)
The Magic of Robert Maxwell 10-6
    (Vocalion VL-73858)

Billy **May**

On CD: Leading the Good Life (Pair); Sorta May (GNP Crescendo, 1996); Best of Billy May, Vol. 1 (Aerospace); Best of Billy May, Vol. 2 (Aerospace); Best of Billy May, Vol. 3 (Aerospace)

Brother Jack **McDuff**

On CD: Sophisticated (FMCA, 1990); Hot Barbeque: Live (BGP, 1993); Write On, Cap'n (Concord Jazz, 1993); The Heatin' System (Cadet, 1994); It's About Time (Concord Jazz, 1995); Hot BBQ (BGP, 1995); That's the Way I Feel About It (Concord Jazz, 1996); Tough 'Duff (Original Jazz Classics, 1995)

Rod **McKuen**

[See also San Sebastian Strings]

On CD: After Midnight (DCC, 1990); At the Movies (Delta, 1990); Best of Rod McKuen (RCA)

The **Melanchrino Orchestra**
(Melanchrino Strings)

Like Paul Weston on Columbia, England's George Melachrino was a pioneer of using instrumental music to create specific moods. With the advent of the long-play, 33 1/3 rpm format in the

Bringing the sound of Britain's George Melachrino to our shores for the first time, the three "Moods in Music" LPs from RCA Victor – "Music for Dining," "Music for Relaxation" and "Music for Reading" – were, with their combination of light classics and pop music, the long-playing ancestors of the lounge album, with its specific purpose of evoking romance. In fact, they were even the forerunners of Melachrino's own early venture into the budding genre, *Music for Two People Alone.*

– JW

Melachrino was a staple on BBC radio well before his "Music For" discs came along, and the musical director of the British Band of the Allied Expeditionary Forces during World War II before that. We especially recommend his *Music for Relaxation,* with lush versions of ranging from Godard's "Berceuse de Jocelyn" to Glenn Miller's "Moonlight Serenade."

– JW

1940s, an artist could create an aural ambience that would last 15 or 20 minutes before any record-changing was necessary – a long-form innovation Melachrino took full advantage of. – JW

José **Melis**

Sergio **Mendes**

On CD: Arara (A&M); Brasileiro (Elektra, 1992); Oceano (Polygram, 1996)

Sergio **Mendes**
and Brasil '66

On CD: Four Sider (A&M); Fool on the Hill (A&M); Classics (A&M, 1986); Greatest Hits of Brasil '66 (A&M); The Best of Sergio Mendes and Brasil '66 (Capitol/Curb, 1993); The Very Best of Sergio Mendes and Brasil '66 (A&M, 1997)

Sergio **Mendes**
and Brasil '77

Sergio **Mendes**
and Brasil '86

Merlin (The Magic Fingers of Merlin and His Trio)

The Swinging Hi-Fi Organ 5-3
   (Bravo K-126)
More Organ Moods, Vol. 2 5-3
   (Bravo K-136)

Buddy **Merrill**

The Guitar Sounds of Buddy Merrill 5-3
   (Accent AC-5010)
Holiday for Guitars 5-3
   (Accent AC-5016)
Latin Festival 5-3
   (Accent AC-5018)
The Exciting World of Buddy Merrill and His Guitars 5-3
   (Accent AC-5020, 1970)
The Many Splendored Guitars of Buddy Merrill 5-3
   (Accent AC-5022)
Sounds of Love 5-3
   (Accent AC-5024)
Electro Sonic Guitars 5-3
   (Accent AC-5028)
Land of a Thousand Guitars 5-3
   (Accent AC-5026)
Today 5-3
   (Accent AC-5025)
Best of Buddy Merrill 5-3
   (Accent ACS-5030)
Beyond the Reef 5-3
   (Accent ACS-5034)
Steel Guitar Country 5-3
   (Accent ACS-5036)
All Time Hits 5-3
   (Accent AC-5038)
World of Guitars 5-3
   (Accent AC-5042)
Guitars on Fire 5-3
   (Accent SQBO-91997)

On CD: Exciting Guitars (GNP Crescendo, 1998); Beyond the Reef: The Hawaiian Guitars of Buddy Merrill (Surfside, 1995)

Bob **Mersey**

[See Moor, Det (and His Orchestra)]

Midnight String Quartet

Rhapsodies for Young Lovers .... 5 - 3
(Viva)
Rhapsodies for Young Lovers, Vol. 2 .... 5 - 3
(Viva V-36008)

Mitch **Miller**

Mitch Miller With Horns and Chorus .... 5 - 3
(Columbia CL-6222, 1952)

Robert **Mitchum**

Don Siegel, who was a great guy and a great director, told me about the time, back in 1948 or so, he made The Big Steal with Mitchum and the great Bill Bendix. During filming, Mitchum got thrown in jail. They shot part of the big car-chase scene without him, shot his part when he got out. But while he was away, the seasons changed, and if you saw the finished picture, you could see the trees go back and forth, back and forth, from full-bloom to bare, as the action alternated between the pursuer and the pursued. Now, that's cool.

The whole mythology of Robert Mitchum is cool: how he was a bad teenage poet, how he rolled drunks on the beach of Santa Monica, how he pissed on the carpet in David O. Selznick's office.

And, like Dean Martin, his cohort in cool, Mitchum was – let's come right out and say it – multifaceted. This here record attests to that.

[from Nick Tosches' liner notes for Scamp's 1995 reissue of *Calypso … Is Like So …*]

Calypso … Is Like So… .... 50 - 30
(Capitol T-853, 1957)
That Man, Robert Mitchum, Sings .... 25 - 15
(Monument SLP-18086, 1967)

On CD: Calypso … Is Like So… (Scamp, 1995); Tall Dark Stranger (Bear Family, 1997); That Man (Bear Family, 1990)

Hugo **Montenegro**

Montenegro Plays .... 5 - 3
(Bainbridge 1028)

Although Mitch Miller is best-remembered as the man who led a hearty gaggle of vocalists – along with the folks at home – through mellow standards on the early '60s NBC-TV show "Sing Along With Mitch," he was a far more complex and interesting figure than the quaint vocal panderer lodged in baby boomers' memories. A graduate of the Eastman School of Music (where he reportedly picked up the difficult English horn and oboe because those chairs were unfilled in the school orchestra) and one-time staff musician at CBS Radio, he first hit it big with children's recordings, before joining with Percy Faith to create the wonderful *Music Until Midnight*.

And speaking of wonderful ... In 1970, Mitch Miller and the Gang came out with a stunning disc called *Peace Sing-Along* (Atlantic SD 8277), which includes a full-throated treatment of "Give Peace A Chance" that certainly ranks as the most unusual version ever of that venerable hippie anthem. In the Strange Treatment of John Lennon Songs

[Continued on next page]

[Continued from previous page]

department, Mitch and the boys make Yoko Ono sound like Vikki Carr. In addition to lyric sheets, the foldout LP features a photo of Mitch, cigar shoved into his bearded face, hair stylishly long and swept back. Even the old farts in the gang look as though they might've been sneaking a puff or two of wacky t'baccy out in the parking lot between takes. Certainly not for inclusion here – in fact, it would be hard to imagine more of an anti-seduction disc than this one – in nonetheless belongs in any truly adventurous vinyl library.

– JW

On CD: Music From "A Fistful of Dollars" and "The Good, The Bad and The Ugly," (RCA, 1995); Movie Classics [with Ennio Morricone] (RCA Camden, 1997)

Det **Moor**
(and His Orchestra)

Bob **Moore**
(and His Orchestra)

On CD: Mexico (Collectables, 1998)

Phil **Moore**

Noro **Morales**

On CD: Noro Morales, His Piano and Rhythm (Ansonia, 1996)

Buddy **Morrow**

Buddy Morrow

Listeners dealing with budget labels in the late '50s and early '60s had to be pretty hip. Sometimes, you'd get the songs you wanted, but with someone you never heard of singing them. Other times, you'd get a favorite artist, but the numbers would sound like something he did at his seventh grade assembly, or some kid's bar mitzvah.

Occasionally, the surprises were even more subtle and subversive (see *Ringo's Theme (This Boy)* and *And I Love Her* by Al Goodman & His Orchestra). Take, for instance, *Jazz From Great TV Shows.* The cover indicates that the listener will be getting music from such then-fave programs as *Route 66, Manhunt, Ben Casey* and even *Window on Main Street.* Logical to figure that these are jazzy versions of theme songs, right?

Well, logical maybe. But wrong. What this amounts to is a collection of pieces by composer-arranger Bob Mersey that have been featured in episodes of those television shows. Get it?

But even though this packaging

[Continued on next page]

Continued from previous page]

nay be a bit duplicitous – despite ner notes that insist, "the reason ehind the production and release of nis album is due to the many equests from the TV audience for ecords of the music heard" – *Jazz rom Great TV Shows* is a first-rate lbum that shows the relationship etween cool jazz and TV around 960, when the two combined to pring the lounge-music influence nto millions of homes. There may ndeed be enough evidence that a ubgenre called "TV jazz" existed nd still exists, and that it's inextri-cably wrapped up in the larger style known as lounge.

Mersey, by the way, helped launch he career of the Ames Brothers while an arranger at NBC radio, arranged Bobby Vinton's hit "Roses Are Red," and produced Andy Williams' *Moon River* LP.

– JW

Tony **Mottola**

Danger [soundtrack and 10-inch LP] 75-45
(MGM E111)

Mr. Big 5-3
(Command RS-807-SD)

Mr. Big 5-3
(Command 1959)

Guitar ... Mottola [reissue of Mr. Big] 5-3
(Command RS-807-SD)

Roman Guitar 5-3
(Command RS-816-SD)

Roman Guitar, Vol. 2 5-3
(Command RS-836-SD, 1962)

Spanish Guitar 5-3
(Command RS-841-SD)

Love Songs: Mexico and South America 5-3
(Command RS-889-SD)

Guitar ... USA 5-3
(Command RS-908-SD)

Guitar ... Paris 5-3
(Command 40001)

Latin Love-In 5-3
(Project 3 5010)

Lush, Latin & Lovely 5-3
(Project 3 5020 SD)

Warm, Wild, and Wonderful 5-3
(Project 3 5025)

The Tony Touch: The Best of Tony Mottola 5-3
(Project 3 5041)

Tony Mattola's Guitar Factory 5-3
(Project 3 5044)

Close to You 5-3
(Project 3 5050)

Warm Feelings 5-3
(Project 3 5058)

Superstar Guitar 5-3
(Project 3 5062)

Tony and Strings 5-3
(Project 3 5069)

Two Guitars for Two in Love 5-3
(Project 3 5074)

Have Yourself a Merry Little Christmas 5-3
(Project 3 5090)

On CD: Stardust (Project 3, 1992); Close to You (Project 3, 1994); Have Yourself a Merry Little Christmas (Project 3); The Romantic Guitar Collection (Special Music, 1994)

Jerry **Murad**
and the Harmonicats

Maybe you think it's risible to imagine that three harmonica players doing stuff like "On Green Dolphin Street" and "Ruby" could create a suitable background for romance. All we can say is, don't knock the Harmonicats until you try 'em.

– JW

On CD: Fascinatin' (Sony Special Products, 1995); Greatest Hits (Columbia, 1990)

Billy **Mure**

Mystic Moods Orchestra

"This is not merely an album of recorded music. It is more, much more. Now, for the first time, a truly unique listening experience awaits you, an experience that will not only capture your attention, but your emotions. For these are the misty moods of a rainy night, moods that recall a particular rain-swept memory – a time of soft and glowing sentimentality when the drops tapped out their special message on the window pane. Or perhaps you've witnessed the awe of that rarest of sights – the stars and the moon battling the clouds for supremacy of the sky. The darkening shadows and the flash of lightning as it casts its own fantastic imagery across a landscape. This then is your special album, ready to transport you to a new world of time and space, with the forces of nature blending beautifully with the man-made music of today."

[from the liner notes for *One Stormy Night*]

On CD: One Stormy Night (Bainbridge, 1996); Sounds of Hawaii (Bainbridge); Moods for a Stormy Night (Bainbridge, 1993; The Right Stuff, 1993); Stormy Memories (Bainbridge, 1990);

A cornerstone of any self-respecting bachelor-pad collection, the Mystic Moods album first appeared in the mid-'60s. Utilizing the then new idea of nature's sound effects combined with music the discs featured new tunes written – often by the series' brilliant conductor-arranger Don Ralke – for each albums particular ambience, sharing grooves with treatments of movie themes and other romantic hits. The series petered out in the '70s, a few years after Ralke left. Although tons of discs have come along since, that utilize the same approach, it's still hard to beat the early Mystic Moods Orchestra at blending nature and music into an unrelentingly sensuous auditory mood.

– JW

This then is your special album, ready to transport you to a new world of time and space, with the forces of nature blending beauti-fully with the man-made music of today.

[from the liner notes for *One Stormy Night*]

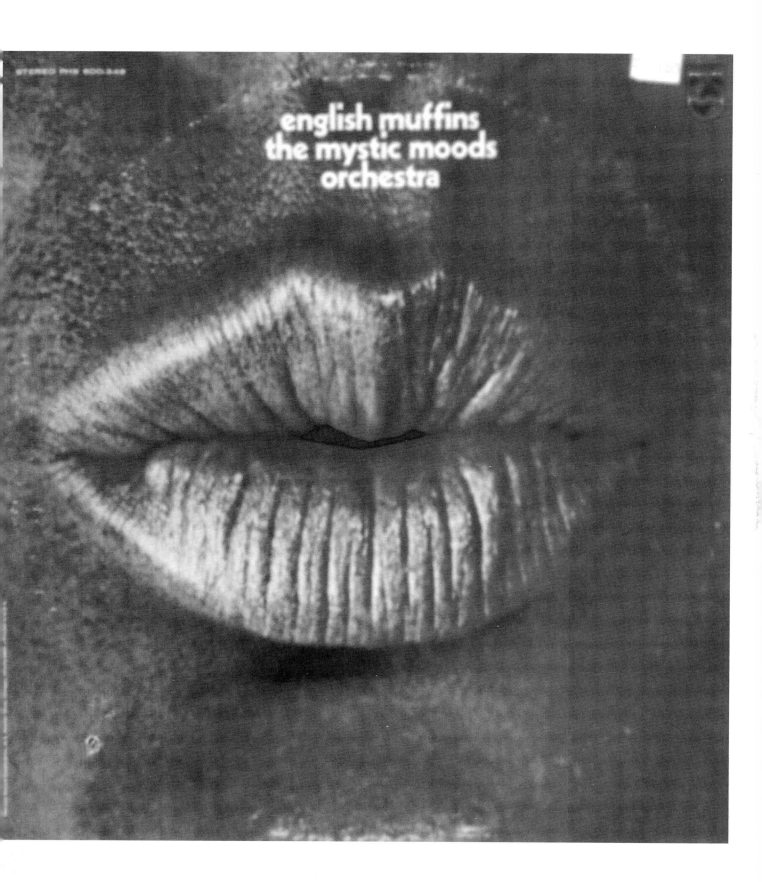

Nighttide (Bainbridge, 1993; The Right Stuff, 1993); Stormy Weekend (Bainbridge, 1993; The Right Stuff, 1993); The Best of Mystic Moods, Vol. 1 (Capitol, 1995); The Best of Mystic Moods, Vol. 2 (Capitol, 1995); Stormy Night in London (CEMA, 1995)

Sandy **Nelson**

On CD: King of the Drums: His Greatest Hits (See For Miles, 1996); Drummin' up a Storm/Compelling Percussion (See For Miles, 1996); Let There Be Drums/Drums Are My Beat! (See For Miles, 1996); Golden Hits: The Best of the Beats (See For Miles, 1997)

Peter **Nero**

On CD: Anything But Lonely (Pro Arte, 1990); My Way (Intersound, 1993); It Had to Be You (Intersound, 1994); Plays Great Songs from the Movies (Sony Special Products, 1995); Love Songs for a Rainy Day (Intersound, 1996); All the Things You Are (Intersound , 1998); Greatest Hits (Sony, 1987)

Al **Nevins**

Anthony **Newley**

Anthony Newly composed the music and songs for Gene Wilder's best film vehicle, Willy Wonka and the Chocalate Factory. *That includes "The Candy Man," the song that became Sammy Davis Jr.'s trademark – and which signaled the end of his significance as a lounge artist.*

On CD: The Best of Anthony Newley (GNP Crescendo, 1995); Once in a Lifetime: The Collection (Razor and Tie, 1997); Willy Wonka and the Chocolate Factory: 25th Anniversary Soundtrack [soundtrack] (Hip-O, 1996)

Alfred **Newman**

On CD: Airport [soundtrack] (Varese Sarabande, 1994)

Wayne **Newton**

On CD: Moods and Moments (Curb, 1992); Greatest Hits (Capitol, 1993)

L o u n g e

Harry **Nilsson**

"There are 12 songs on this album and as you will hear, they are quite exceptionally distinguished pieces of art and as Art, they are timeless and very precious. Beyond price. It was important, therefore, to treat them with immense loving care and kindness ...

Finally, something about why we did the album. We did it because these songs deserve it, and because it is 1973 and times are tough and when times are tough, we need, all of us, whatever our age, whatever our lifestyle, whatever our pain ... we need a 'Little Touch of Schmilsson In The Night'."

[from producer Derek Taylor's liner notes for *A Little Touch of Schmilsson in the Night*]

A Little Touch of Schmilsson In The Night .... 5 - 3
[conducted and arranged by Gordon Jenkins]
   (RCA APL1-0097, 1973)

Ken **Nordine**

Concert in the Sky .... 75 - 45
   (Decca DL-8550, 1957)
Word Jazz .... 50 - 30
   (Dot DLP-3075, 1957)
Son of Word Jazz .... 50 - 30
   (Dot DLP-25096/3096, 1958)
Love Words .... 50 - 30
   (Dot DLP-25115/3115, 1958)
My Baby .... 50 - 30
   (Dot DLP-25142/3142, 1958)
Next! .... 50 - 30
   (Dot DLP-25196/3196, 1959)
Word Jazz, Vol. 2 .... 50 - 30
   (Dot DLP-25301/3301, 1960)
Best of Word Jazz .... 40 - 24
   (Dot DLP-25880, 1968)
Voice of Love .... 40 - 24
   (Hamilton H-12102, 1959)
Colors .... 40 - 24
   (Phillips PHS-600-224, 1966)
Ken Nordine Does Robert Shure's "Twink" .... 30 - 18
   (Phillips PHS-600-258, 1967)
Stare With Your Ears .... 10 - 6
   (Snail SR-1001, 1979)

On CD: Colors (Asphodel, 1995); Devout Catalyst (Grateful Dead, 1992); Upper Limbo (Grateful Dead, 1994); Best of Word Jazz, Vol. 1 (Rhino, 1990)

You might not expect ex-banker Harry Nilsson – singer-songwriter, rock-era hitmaker ("Without You"), and John Lennon drinkin' bud – to show up in a lounge-music book, but this album fits the bill, and more. It's a collection of standards, from "Makin' Whoopee" to "As Time Goes By," each one taken at a pace that would have to speed up to crawl, with Harry delivering the words as though he had the weight of the world, or at least a brace of martinis, on his shoulders.

– JW

Chico **O'Farrill**

On CD: Pure Emotion (Milestone, 1995)

Leni **Okehu**
(and His Surfboarders)

The **101 Strings**

"A cheesy, post-Spectoresque Wal-Mart of Sound that will sizzle your synapses and induce haunting hallucinations."
   [WFMU commentator on *Astro-Sounds From Beyond the Year 2000*]

Lounge

To include the entire discography of the 101 Strings, we would have to publish *Forever Lounge* in about three separate volumes, two of which would be dedicated solely to this prolific and revolving line-up of hokey horse-hair specialists. While the 101 Strings settled for overly lush background music more often than not, they sometimes produced rich, evocative music or even bizarre experimentation. Like Mantovani, this is music that leans more toward elevator emptiness than lounge lizardry, but a good chunk of this European ensemble's catalog is worth including in the collection of any devilish romantic.

– TC

On CD: Astro-Sounds From Beyond the Year 2000 (Scamp); Mariachi (Alshire, 1990); 101 Strings (Alshire, 1994); Tribute to Henry Mancini (Alshire, 1994); Aloha Hawaii, Vol. 1-2 (Alshire, 1995); Golden Hits, Vol. 1-2 (Alshire, 1995); Movie & TV Themes (Alshire, 1995); Romantic Latin America (Alshire, 1995); Romantic Latin Favorites (Alshire, 1995); Space Music (Alshire, 1995); Strings for Lovers (Alshire, 1995); Tribute to Nat King Cole (Alshire, 1995); Play a Tribute to the Beatles (Alshire, 1995); The Soul of Spain (Excelsior, 1996); Love Songs (Alshire, 1996); 20 Years of Beautiful Music (Alshire, 1996); 101 Strings & Pianos (Alshire, 1996); Candlelight & Romance (Alshire, 1996); Cole Porter's Night & Day (Alshire, 1996); Romantic Fantasy (Alshire, 1996); Romantic Moods (Alshire, 1996); Music Moods: The Quiet Hour (Madacy, 1997); Music Moods: Cocktail Time (Madacy, 1997); Music Moods: Latin Mood (Madacy, 1997); Plays Frank Sinatra (Madacy, 1997); The Best of the 101 Strings (Alshire, 1996); Golden Hits of the 101 Strings (Alshire, 1996); Best of the 101 Strings (Alshire, 1996)

The **Out-Islanders**

The **Outriggers**

Rapture... 5 - 3
    (Warner Bros. W/WS 1224, 1959)
Surrender... 5 - 3
    (Warner Bros. W/WS-1376)

Reg **Owen**

Coffee Break .... 5 - 3
    (RCA Victor LPM-1582, 1958)

Larry **Page**
(Larry Page Orchestra)

The Larry Page Orchestra was one of the more upstanding and innovative collectives making beat music into something even the parents of the surf nuts could enjoy. If the name Larry Page rings a bell, you've probably been banging your head a bit. For instance, Music for Night People *features Larry's son Jimmy Page in the orchestra along with an up-and-comer named John Paul Jones.*
– TC

Music for Night People .... 200 - 120
    (Music Club, 1965)

On CD: Music for Night People (1996)

Marty **Paich**

What's New.. 25 - 15
    (Discovery 857, 1988)
Revel Without Pause .... 25 - 15
    (Interlude 1009, 1959)
The Rock-Jazz Incident .... 25 - 15
    (Reprise 6206)
Jazz for Relaxation.. 25 - 15
    (Tampa, 1956)
I Get a Boot Out of You: The Modern Touch of Marty Paich .... 25 - 15
    (Warner Brothers WB-1349, 1959)

On CD: Jazz for Relaxation (VSOP); Picasso of Big Band Jazz (Candid, 1990); Moanin' (Discovery, 1992)

Korla **Pandit**

The reticent Korla Pandit was the master of the Hammond organ in the late '50s, often showing

"A GRACIOUS CITY gently lowers its blinds at night. And unlike Paris – or Barcelona or Mexico City – a more tranquil mood envelops London as dusk gives way to the dark.

"Norrie Paramor's impeccable strings, the Ariel-like voice of Scotland's Patricia Clarke and a choice selection of moody – yet brazenly romantic – songs combine to portray London, and its love hours, dramatically in music ...

"This is the feel, the atmosphere, of a charming city in simple musical terms. Soft brass, gentle woodwinds, sensuous strings and a voice that defies words to describe accurately. This is Paramor and London After Dark."

[from the liner notes for *London After Dark*]

off his fluid chops on television. Sporting his bejeweled turban, he's had numerous film cameos, including one as himself in Tim Burton's Ed Wood.

On CD: Odyssey [both Music of the Exotic East and Latin Holiday] (Fantasy, 1996); Exotica 2000 (Sympathy for the Record Industry, 1996)

Norrie **Paramor**

On CD: Norrie Paramor Orchestra (Castle, 1994); Autumn (Angel)

The **Paris** Left Bank Musicians

Byron **Parker**

Les **Paul** (and Mary Ford)

On CD: 16 Most Requested Songs (Columbia, 1996); The Best of the Capitol Masters: Selections… (Capitol, 1992); All-Time Greatest Hits (CEMA, 1992); The Legend and the Legacy [boxed set] (Capitol, 1992); Greatest Hits [Pair] (Pair, 1992); Love Songs by Les Paul & Mary Ford (Ranwood, 1997)

Pedro and His Amigos

Perrey and Kingsley

"Here are a dozen electronic pop tunes. They are the electrifying good-time music of the coming age, the switched-on dance music that will soon be it. This is the lively answer to the question that puzzles – and who knows, even frightens – people who have heard the serious electronic compositions of recent years and wonder, is this the music of the future? As for that avant-garde wing, we say more power to it. But there are other things in the future, such as pleasure. And so presented here is the electronic 'Au Go Go' that might be heard soon from the juke boxes at the interplanetary way stations where space ships make their rest stops. The idiom is strange and yet

familiar; here a touch of rock, there a touch of bosa nova, a whiff of the blues in one piece and a whiff of Tchaikovsky in another. But these atoms of pop music are exploded into fresh patterns. They outline a strange new sound world, yet one in which we can feel at home. The future is upon us, they say, and the future is fun."

[from the liner notes for *The In Sound From Way Out*]

The In Sound From Way Out .... 40 - 24
   (Vanguard VSD-79222, 1966)
Kaleidoscopic Vibrations .... 40 - 24
   (Vanguard VSD-79264, 1967)
Spotlight on the Moog [Kaleidoscopic Vibrations with different cover] .... 40 - 24
   (Vanguard VSD-65-25, 1967)

On CD: Essential Perrey and Kingsley (Vanguard, 1988); The In Sound From Way Out (Vanguard, 1996)

Jean-Jaques **Perrey**

Dynamoog .... 50 - 30
   (CREA Sound Ltd. [Canada] 46.532, 1971)
Switched-On Santa [as Sy Mann] .... 50 - 30
   (Pickwick SPCX-1007)
The Happy Moog [with Harry Breuer] .... 50 - 30
   (Pickwick SPC-3160, 1969)
The Amazing New Electronic Pop Sound of Jean-Jacques Perrey .... 25 - 15
   (Vanguard VSD-79286, 1967)
Moog Indigo .... 25 - 15
   (Vanguard VSD-6549, 1970)
Moog Indigo [reissue] .... 5 - 3
   (BGP BGPM-103, 1995)
Sound for Insomniacs .... 75 - 45
   (France, 1964)

On CD: Moog Indigo (Vanguard, 1996); The Amazing New Electronic Pop Sound of Jean-Jacques Perrey (Ace [UK]); E.V.A. [remixes] (BGP, 1997)

Trudy **Pitts**

Introducing the Fabulous Trudy Pitts .... 5 - 3
   (Prestige PRST-7523, 1967)
The Excitement of Trudy Pitts .... 5 - 3
   (Prestige PRST-7583, 1968)

The golden age of lounge might have been all but over by the time "I Want to Hold Your Hand" hit No. 1 in America, but that doesn't mean there still aren't some great practitioners still knocking around out there. In *The Café Pierre Trio,* released in the early '80s, guitarist Bucky Pizzarelli, pianist Russ Kassoff and bassist Jerry Bruno hew to the tasteful part- tasteful jazz, part-romantic pop formula that characterizes the greatest classic lounge acts. *New Yorker* critic Whitney Baliett described the group's live repertoire as "fervent jazz disguised as hotel music," a compliment that could apply to several other top lounge acts as well.

– JW

Bucky **Pizzarelli**

Music Minus Many Men .... 5 - 3
    (Savoy MG-12158, 1960)
The Café Pierre Trio .... 5 - 3
    (Monmouth Evergreen MES-7093, 1982)
Swinging Stevens .... 5 - 3
    (Stash 239, 1984)

On CD: Hit That Jive Jack (Stash)

Jack **Pleis**
(and His Orchestra)

Music for Two Sleepy People .... 5 - 3
    (Decca DL-8763/78763)

Andre **Popp**

Listening to the music of Elsa Popping and her Pixieland Band is, to be truthful, an unnerving experience. It is not unlike watching a 3-D movie without the special spectacles, or carrying on a conversation under water.
  [from the liner notes for *Delirium In Hi-Fi*]

Delerium in Hi-Fi .... 50 - 30
[billed as Elsa Popping and Her Pixieland Band]
    (Columbia WL-106, 1956)
Presenting Popp! .... 10 - 6
    (Columbia WL-130, 1958)
Why Say Goodbye .... 10 - 6
    (MGM MGM-4564)

On CD: La Musique Qui Fait Popp (VPRO)

Franck **Pourcel** (and His
French [or Rockin'] Strings)

Aquarius .... 5 - 3
    (Atco SD-33-299, 1969)
Les Baxter's La Femme .... 5 - 3
    (Capitol T-10015)
The French Touch .... 5 - 3
    (Capitol T-10103)
In a Nostalgic Mood .... 5 - 3
    (EMI 46017, 1984)

On CD: Latinoamerica (Vedisco, 1996); Franck Pourcel (Best Music Int'l, 1998)

Powerhouse Five

[see Harris, Dave]

Perez **Prado**
and His Orchestra

On CD: The Mambo King, Vol. 1 (RCA); Mondo Mambo! The Best of Perez Prado and His Orchestra (Rhino); Mambo Mania/Havana 3 A.M. (Bear Family, 1990); Voodoo Suite/Exotic Suite (Bear Family, 1990); Dance Date With … Perez Prado (Polydor, 1994); Besame Mucho (Saludos Amigos, 1994); Mambos (Saludos Amigos, 1994); Perez Prado and Beny More: Mambos (Saludos Amigos, 1994); King of Mambo (BMG, 1995); Mambo (Sony International, 1990); Greatest Hits (Huub, 1991); Havana 3 a.m. (RCA International, 1990); Prez (RCA); Que Rico Mambo! (RCA); Mambo King (Sony International, 1993)

Andre **Previn**

On CD: After Hours (Telarc, 1989); Uptown (Telarc, 1990); Old Friends (Telarc, 1991); The Essence of Andre Previn (Columbia-Legacy, 1994); Piano Stylings of Andre Previn (RCA, 1990); More of the Best (Delta, 1996); Some of the Best (Delta, 1996); Ballads (Angel, 1996); 4 to Go!/The Light Fantastic (Collectables, 1998); Pal Joey (Original Jazz Classics, 1991); Like Previn! (Original Jazz Classics, 1994); Valley of the Dolls (Philips, 1998); A Touch of Elegance (Columbia-Legacy, 1994)

Louis **Prima**

On CD: Louis Prima Orchestra (Laserlight, 1991); Return of the Wildest (Jasmine, 1994); The Capitol Recordings (Bear Family, 1994); On Stage (Jasmine, 1996); Let's Swing It (Charly Budget, 1996); Swing with Louis Prima (Fat Boy, 1996); Capitol Collectors Series (Capitol, 1991); Zooma Zooma: The Best of Louis Prima (Rhino); Jazz Collector Edition (Delta, 1991); His Greatest Hits (Jasmine, 1994); Greatest Hits (Cede, 1996); Pretty Music: Prima Style (Jasmine, 1998)

Tito **Puente**

Puente salsa buffs won't want to miss his performances for the hip cartoon series The Simpsons. *With his Latin Jazz Ensemble, he performed a spicy, witty tune called "Senor Burns," in which Tito himself growls his own distaste for the slimy nuclear plant boss with lyrics like, "Please die and fry!" That song and a Puente reading of the show's end-credits theme is available on* The

Simpsons' Songs in the Key of Springfield *(Rhino, 1997).*
– TC

On CD: New Cha Cha/Mambo Herd (LaserLight); Mambo Diablo (Concord Picante, 1990); The Mambo King: His 100th Album (RMM, 1991); Mamborama! (Charly, 1991); Mambo of the Times (Concord Jazz, 1991); Tito Puente & His Latin Jazz All Stars (Concord Jazz, 1993); More Spanish Songs That Mama Never Taught Me (Tico, 1993); Tito Swings … (Tico, 1994); Top Percussion/Dance Mania (Bear Family, 1994); Bossa Nova by Puente (Palladium, 1995); Special Delivery (Concord Picante, 1996); Night Beat/Mucho Puente (Bear Family, 1994); 50 Years of Swing: 50 Great Years & Tracks [boxed set] (RMM, 1997); El Rey del Timbal: The Best of Tito Puente (Rhino, 1997); The Best of Tito Puente, Vol. 1 (RCA, 1992)

Johnny **Puleo**
and His Harmonica Gang

Quartette Tres Bien

Don **Ralke**
and His Orchestra

"… Whether you're a full-fledged bongo addict or just an interested spectator, until you've heard Gershwin with bongos … well, your ears just haven't lived.

   "Don't cheat your ears. They deserve this."

   [from the liner notes for *But You've Never Heard Gershwin With Bongos*]

Classically trained multi-instrumentalist Don Ralke got the idea for But You've Never Heard Gershwin With Bongos *during the bongo craze of the late '50s, when every with-it party had at least one hipster riding the beat on his own set of skins. As the liner notes to this delightfully improbable album put it, "He will Thump Along with any kind of music, from Tchaikovsky to Carrie Jacobs Bond."*

Here, bongo manics had the chance to hear how it's done on a program that runs from "Clap Yo Hands" to "They Can't Take That Away from Me," in a program put together by arranger-conductor Ralke, one of the unsung giants of lounge.

– JW

Allegedly recorded by "The Baron," a nightclub performer played by actor Eddie Cole in the New Orleans-set *Bourbon Street Beat* (ABC-TV, 1959-60), the music in *'The Baron' Plays Bourbon Street Beat* is actually a collection of TV jazz played by studio musicians under the direction of lounge-music heavyweight Don Ralke. The material – some standards, some written by Ralke and others for the show – is, as might be imagined, a little bluesier than the normal run of TV jazz, with some nicely moody piano work.

– JW

Music for the Weaker Sex .... 5 - 3
   (RCA Victor LPM-1583)
Compulsion to Swing .... 5 - 3
   (RCA Victor LPM/LSP-1947, 1958)
Riot in Rhythm .... 5 - 3
   (RCA Victor LMP/LPR-2002, 1959)
Dynamic Dimensions .... 5 - 3
   (RCA Victor LSA-2396, 1961)

Harry **Revel**

Music for Peace of Mind .... 20 - 12
   (Capitol H-221)
Music Out of the Moon .... 20 - 12
   (Capitol, 1947)

Alvino **Rey**

Swingin' Fling .... 25 - 15
   (Capitol ST-1085, 1958)
Ping Pong .... 25 - 15
   (Capitol ST-1262, 1960)
That Lonely Feeling .... 25 - 15
   (Capitol ST-1395, 1960)
My Reverie .... 25 - 15
   (Decca DL-8403, 1958)
As I Remember Hawaii .... 25 - 15
   (Dot DLP-25448, 1962)

On CD: By Request (Hindsight, 1993); Alvino Rey and His Orchestra (Collectors Choise, 1996)

Emil **Richards**
(Emil Richards' Yazz Band)

Journey to Bliss .... 5 - 3
   (Impulse 9166)
Yazz Per Favore .... 5 - 3
   (Del-Fi, 1960)

On CD: Yazz Per Favore (Del-Fi, 1997)

Red **Richards**

Soft Buns .... 5 - 3
   (West 54 WLW-8000, 1978)

Nelson **Riddle**

Harlow [soundtrack] .... 30 - 18
  (Warner Brothers WS-1599)

On CD: Let's Fall in Love (CEMA, 1992); Plays Sinatra Classics (CEMA); Symphony for the North (Top); Best of Nelson Riddle (Curb, 1997); Let's Face the Music & Dance/Lisbon Antigua (Touch of Class, 1998); The Silver Collection (Verve)

The **Riveria Strings**

Love Is Blue .... 5 - 3
  (Mercury Wing SRW-16355)

Marco **Rizo**

Morning Melody.. 5 - 3
  (Forum SF-9076)
Bossa Nova/Brazillian Jazz .... 5 - 3
  (Somerset P-18800)

Howard **Roberts**

Something's Cookin'.. 5 - 3
  (Capitol ST-1887, 1964)
Howard Roberts Is a Dirty Guitar Player... 5 - 3
  (Capitol ST-1961, 1963)
Goodies.. 5 - 3
  (Capitol ST-2400, 1965)
Whatever's Fair .... 5 - 3
  (Capitol ST-2478, 1966)
All-Time Great Instrumental Hits... 5 - 3
  (Capitol ST-2609, 1966)
Out Of Sight (But In Mind).. 5 - 3
  (Capitol ST-2901, 1968)
Mr. Roberts Plays Guitar .... 5 - 3
  (Norgran MGN-1106, 1956)
Velvet Groove .... 5 - 3
  (Verve, 1956)
The Movin' Man.. 5 - 3
  (Verve, 1957)

Harry **Robinson**

Moody and Magnificent .... 5 - 3
  (Riverside RLP-7528, 1962)

Tito **Rodriguez**

On CD: Dance Date With Tito Rodriguez (Polygram, 1994); The Best of Tito Rodriguez & His Orquesta (RCA International, 1992); The Best of Tito Rodriguez, Vol. 2 (RCA International, 1994); The Best of Tito Rodriguez, Vol. 3 (RCA International, 1994); Grandes Exitos (Polygram, 1994); The Best of the Best (Sony International, 1995)

Roger **Roger**

Roger Roger – that's ro-shzay ro-shzay to you, Yank – was a prolific French soundtrack composer for decades. He scored nearly 500 films and cartoons – the musical equivalent of onomatapaeia, for films needing to quickly evoke traffic, monsters or similar hustle and bustle – but his work was never released as records. The '95 CD is the first time his film music reached a commercial audience.
– TC

On CD: Grands Travaux (Koch Screen, 1995)

Shorty **Rogers**

On CD: Manteca: Afro-Cuban Influence (BMG, 1992); The Complete Atlantic and EMI Jazz Recordings (Mosaic); Swings [Chances Are plus extras] (Bluebird, 1991)

David **Romaine**

Edmundo **Ros**

On CD: Chiquita Banana (Harlequin, 1998); Tropical Magic, Vol. 2 (Harlequin, 1995); Come With Me, My Honey (1998); Latin Melodies Old and New (1995); Edmundo Ros and His Rumba Band (Harlequin)

David **Rose**

On CD: Stripper (Empire, 1997); Very Best of David Rose (MGM, 1996); Very Best of David Rose (Taragon, 1996); Stripper and Other Favorites (Reper [UK], 1997)

"Strings that soar like spears of sunlight, and stipple the air with the sound of pleasure ... deep-throated horns that curl around the end of a supple phrase ... the melancholy arc of an oboe singing darkly ... the joyous sweep of trombones and trumpets ... these are the hallmarks of the music of David Rose, pianist, composer, arranger, symphony conductor, a man of music to whom instrumental colors are as personal as the sound of voices ..."

[from the liner notes for *Concert With a Beat!*]

"In this recording, the orchestra has been set up for maximum stereo effect with two choirs of trombones (five each) worked at right angles to each other in the studio. The rhythm section (bass and drums) were at center with each of the two pianos just off center in the orchestra. But ... enough. Listen to the totally pleasurable result as Pete Rugolo (and this unique combination of 10 trombones and two pianos) provide the perfect range of stereo moods, for dancing or listening."

[from Jere Real's liner notes for *Ten Trombones Like Two Pianos*]

Rugolo, a native of Sicily who came to the U.S. at age 5, did a ton of film and TV music– in fact, he's on some of the *Peter Gunn* stuff – and arranged one of Stan Kenton's biggest songs, the classic "Intermission Riff," in the mid-'40s.

– JW

Bob **Rosengarden**
and Phil Kraus

Pete **Rugolo**

On CD: Introducing Pete Rugolo/Adventures in Rhythm (Collectables)

The **San Sebastian Strings**

On CD: The Sea (Warner Bros., 1990)

Colonel **Sanders**

Santo and Johnny

On CD: Best of Santo and Johnny (Stardust, 1997)

"And we made love, and only the sea was watching ..."

Hot '60s poet Rod McKuen – whose wonderful beatnik album *Rod McKuen Takes a San Francisco Hippie Trip* (Tradition Everest, TR 2063) is highly recommended for fans of the wacky – teamed up with conductor-arranger Anita Kerr for a series of well-received discs in the late '60s. The "sea" LPs, their most successful, used ambient surf noises to accompany Kerr's romantic string arrangements and McKuen's lonely-guy-on-the-beach ramblings, voiced by an unnamed narrator who sounded like a white Barry White. Critics have often been less than kind to McKuen and his work, but it sounds perfectly fine here, with the surf crashing, the strings rising, and an oboe or muted trumpet weaving in and out with a distant, sensual, sadness.

– JW

Eddie **Sauter** and Bill Finegan
(Sauter-Finegan Orchestra)

One Night Stand With Sauter-Finegan .... 50 - 30
   (Joyce 1132)
Inside Sauter-Finegan .... 20 - 12
   (RCA Victor LJM-1003, 1954)
The Sound of the Sauter-Finegan Orchestra .... 20 - 12
   (RCA Victor LPM-1009, 1954)
Adventure in Time .... 20 - 12
   (RCA Victor LPM-1240, 1956)
Under Analysis .... 20 - 12
   (RCA Victor LPM-1341, 1957)
Straight Down the Middle .... 20 - 12
   (RCA Victor LPM/LSP-1497, 1957)
New Directions in Music [10-inch] .... 20 - 12
   (RCA Victor LPM-3115, 1958)
Inside Sauter-Finegan Revisited .... 20 - 12
   (RCA Victor LSP-2473, 1961)
Lullaby of the Leaves .... 20 - 12
   (United Artists UAL-3281)

On CD: Directions in Music (RCA, 1990); That's All (Magic, 1996); New Directions in Music (Bluebird, 1988)

Walter **Scharf**

Dreams By the Dozen (For Men Only) .... 5 - 3
   (Jubilee JLP-1033)

Lalo **Schifrin**

Bossa Nova: New Brazilian Jazz .... 20 - 12
   (Audio Fidelity AFSD-5981, 1962)
Murderer's Row [soundtrack] .... 100 - 60
   (Colgems S-5003)
Black Widow .... 10 - 6
   (CTI Records CTI7-5000, 1976)
Mission: Impossible [soundtrack] .... 30 - 18
   (Dot DLP-25831, 1967)
There's a Whole Lalo Schifrin Goin' On .... 10 - 6
   (Dot DLP-25852)
Way ... Way Out [soundtrack] .... 20 - 12
   (Fox S-3192)

On CD: Dissection and Reconstruction of Music From the Past as Performed by the Inmates of Lal (Polygram, 1997); Music From "Mission: Impossible" (Hip-O, 1996); Black Widow (Sony, 1997); The Liquidator (MCA, 1990); Mission: Impossible ... and More (Motor, 1997); Bullitt [remix] (Warner Bros., 1997); Masters of Mayhem (Intersound, 1997); "Mission: Impossible"/"Take Five" [CD single] (Four Winds, 1996)

Vic **Schoen**

Dick **Schory**

Dick Schory's percussive ambitions almost made him anti-lounge. The liner notes to Bang Baaroom and Harp *refer to the enselmble as the "biggest battery of percussion west of Cape Canaveral."* Re-Percussion *employs more than 100 different percussion instruments. The results are wowee, but the sound is still zowee.*
– TC

On Tour .... 25 - 15
    (RCA Victor LSP-2806, 1964)

The Happy Hits .... 25 - 15
    (RCA Victor LSP-2926, 1964)

On CD: Music for Bang Baaroom and Harp (Classic Compact Discs)

Hazel **Scott**

Hazel Scott [10-inch] .... 5 - 3
    (Coral CRL-56057, 1952)

Hazel Scott's Late Show [10-inch] .... 5 - 3
    (Capitol H-364, 1953)

Relaxed Piano Moods [10-inch] .... 5 - 3
    (Debut DLP-16, 1955)

After Hours .... 5 - 3
    (Tioch 1013)

Afterthoughts .... 5 - 3
    (1980)

On CD: Relaxed Piano Moods (Debut, 1995); Relaxed Piano Moods (Original Jazz Classics, 1992)

Raymond **Scott**
(and His Orchestra)

Powerhouse, Vol. 1 [10-inch] .... 50 - 30
    (Columbia 6083, 1949)

Soothing Sounds for Baby, Vol. 1 .... 100 - 60
    (Epic)

Soothing Sounds for Baby, Vol. 2 .... 100 - 60
    (Epic)

Soothing Sounds for Baby, Vol. 3 .... 100 - 60
    (Epic)

This Time With Strings .... 20 - 12

On CD: Powerhouse, Vol. 1 (Stash); Powerhouse, Vol. 1 (Vintage Jazz); Reckless Nights and Turkish Twilights: The Music of Raymond Scott (Columbia, 1992)

Herbert **Seiter**

In The Continental Manner [10-inch] .... 5 - 3
    (Westminster WL-3017, 1954)

Doc **Severinsen**

George **Shearing**

With a suggested list price of $1.98 (mono), Lion Records (George Shearing Goes Hollywood) was the budget arm of MGM Records, featuring lots of big-band artists, big-band era vocalists, Jimmy Durante, Greer Garson, and Music From Peter Gunn *(L70112), featuring Mancini compositions not performed by Mancini.*

On CD: On the Sunny Side Of (GNP, 1992); How Beautiful Is Night (Telarc, 1992); That Shearing Sound (Telarc, 1994); Paper Moon: Songs of Nat King Cole (Telarc, 1995); Shearing Touch (Pair, 1991); Mellow Moods (Pair); Cocktail for Two (Jazz World, 1994); The Best of George Shearing (Capitol-Curb, 1993); All Time Favorites (Jazz World, 1994); George Shearing & Friends (Pair, 1995); The Best of George Shearing (1955-1960) (Capitol, 1995); Best of George Shearing, Vol. 2 (1960-1969) (Capitol, 1997); Evening with George Shearing and Mel Torme (Concord Jazz); The Swingin's Mutual (Capitol, 1992); White Satin & Black Satin (Capitol, 1991)

Tak **Shindo**

Frank **Sinatra**

"... familiar ballads of loneliness and longing, given rich new expression by the voice of Frank Sinatra. He performs for the first time with arranger-conductor Gordon Jenkins, whose deeply romantic orchestrations provide a haunting musical background. Throughout the album, Frank creates a rare perfection of mood, in sensitive performances sure to have intensely personal meaning for every listener."

[from the liner notes for *Where Are You?*]

Frank Sinatra [10-inch]... 50 - 30
   (Capitol H-488, 1954)
In the Wee Small Hours .... 15 - 9
   (Capitol W-581, 1955)
Songs for Young Lovers/Swing Easy .... 15 - 9
   (Capitol W-587, 1955)
Songs for Swingin' Lovers! .... 15 - 9
   (Capitol W-653, 1956)
High Society [soundtrack] .... 25 - 15
   (Capitol W/SW-750, 1957)
This Is Sinatra! .... 15 - 9
   (Capitol T-768, 1957)
Close to You.. 15 - 9
   (Capitol T-789, 1957)
A Swingin' Affair! .... 15 - 9
   (Capitol W-803, 1957)
Where Are You .... 15 - 9
   (Capitol W/SW-855, 1957)
Pal Joey [soundtrack]... 20 - 12
   (Capitol W/SW-912, 1958)
Come Fly with Me .... 15 - 9
   (Capitol W/SW-920, 1958)
This Is Sinatra, Vol. 2 .... 15 - 9

                  (Capitol W-982, 1958)
                  Only the Lonely .... 15 - 9
                  (Capitol W/SW-1053, 1958)
                  Come Dance with Me! .... 15 - 9
                  (Capitol W/SW-1069, 1959)
                  Look to Your Heart .... 15 - 9
                  (Capitol W-1164, 1959)
                  No One Cares .... 15 - 9
                  (Capitol W/SW-1221, 1959)
                  Sentimental Journey .... 15 - 9
                  (Capitol W-90986, 1959)

Working with Warner Bros. and Reprise in the '60s, Mr. Stan Cornyn wrote what were possibly the best liner notes ever penned. Little compact gems of impressionism, Cornyn's copy was full of such gravitas that it made Nancy Sinatra's determination to do a country-music album seem as important as Louis Pasteur's decision to go into medicine. His work on *September of My Years* is among his best. In a few terse paragraphs studded with scraps of dialogue, he paints an unforgettable portrait of a mellow, older Sinatra, his relationship with conductor Gordon Jenkins, the awe he inspires in everyone he passes:

"He has lived enough for two lives, and can sing now of September. Of the bruising days. Of the rouged lips and bourbon times. Of chill winds, of forgotten ladies who ride in limousines.

"September can be an attitude or an age or a wistful reality. For this man, it is a time of love. A time to sing.

"A thousand days hath September."

Write on, Stan Cornyn.

– JW

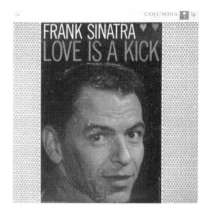

Sinatra on CD

Gold (Pair, 1992)

Long Ago & Far Away (Vintage Jazz
  Classics, 1992)

At the Movies (Capitol, 1993)

Christmas Songs by Sinatra (Columbia,
  1994)

My Shining Hour (Drive Archive, 1994)

Live, Seattle, Wa 1957 (Special Music,
  1995)

Christmas Through the Years
  (LaserLight, 1995)

Blue Moods: Blues According to Sinatra
  (Skylark Jazz, 1995)

Everything Happens to Me (Reprise,
  1996)

Christmas Sing with Frank and Bing
  (Delta, 1996)

Love of Mine (Cema Special Markets,
  1996)

Songs for Swingin' Lovers (Capitol)

In the Wee Small Hours (Capitol)

Point of No Return (Capitol)

Come Fly With Me (Capitol)

Sings for Only the Lonely (Capitol)

All the Way (Capitol)

Can-Can [soundtrack] (Capitol)

Pal Joey [soundtrack] (Capitol)

A Swingin' Affair (Capitol)

Christmas Dreaming (Columbia)

Sinatra Swings (Reprise)

Sinatra/Basie (Reprise)

Sinatra's Sinatra (Reprise)

Academy Award Winners (Reprise)

Softly, As I leave You (Reprise)

September of My Years (Reprise)

Strangers in the Night (Reprise)

Moonlight Sinatra (Reprise)

Sinatra at the Sands (Reprise)

Cycles (Reprise)

Francis Albert Sinatra and Antonio
  Carlos Jobim (Reprise)

That's Life (Reprise)

My Way (Reprise)

A Man Alone (Reprise)

Ol' Blue Eyes Is Back (Reprise)

Some Nice Things I've Missed (Reprise)

The Main Event – Live (Reprise)

The Capitol Collectors Series (Capitol,
  1990)

The Capitol Years: The Best of Frank
  Sinatra [five-CD boxed set]
  (Capitol CI-94777, 1990)

The Capitol Years: The Best of Frank
  Sinatra [three-CD boxed set]
  (Capitol , 1990)

The Reprise Collection (Reprise, 1990)

Frank Sinatra's Greatest (Capitol, 1991)

Sinatra Reprise: The Very Good Years
  (Warner Bros., 1991)

Sings the Select Cole Porter (Capitol,
  1991)

Night and Day (Huub, 1991)

Sinatra: CBS Mini-Series Soundtrack
  (Reprise, 1992)

Sinatra (Warner Bros., 1992)

16 Most Requested Songs (Columbia, '92)

The Best of the Capitol Years:
  Selections (Capitol, 1992)

The Christmas Collection (Dejavu,
  1992)

The Essence of Frank Sinatra
  (Columbia, 1994)

Legendary Love Songs of a Lifetime
  (Skylark Jazz, 1994)

Sinatra 80th: All the Best (Capitol,
  1995)

I've Got a Crush on You (Columbia,
  1995)

Sings the Select Johnny Mercer
  (Capitol, 1995)

The Complete Reprise Studio
  Recordings [boxed set] (Warner Brother,
  1995)

The Best of the Columbia Years: 1943-
  1952 [boxed set] (Sony, 1995)

Begin the Beguine (Musketeer, 1995)

My Way: The Best of Frank Sinatra
  (Reprise, 1997)

Love Songs (RCA, 1997)

Portrait of Sinatra: Columbia Classics
  (Sony, 1997)

Sings His Greatest Hits (Sony, 1997)

20 Great Love Songs (Best Music
  International, 1998) Songs for
  Swingin' Lovers (Dj Specialist, 1998)

Lovely Way to Spend an Evening
  (ASV/Living Era, 1998)

"My Way" [single] (Warner Bros.,
  1993)

George **Siravo**

On CD: Swinging Stereo in Studio A (RCA, 1996)

Felix **Slatkin**

Roy **Smeck**
(and His Paradise Serenaders)

Ethel **Smith**

Ethel Smith Swings Sweetly.. 5 - 3
(Decca DL-4095)

Make Mine Hawaiian.. 5 - 3
(Decca DL-4236)

Rhythm Antics! .... 5 - 3
(Decca DL-4414)

Latin from Manhattan .... 5 - 3
(Decca DL-4457)

At the End of a Perfect Day... 5 - 3
(Decca DL-4467)

Hollywood Favorites .... 5 - 3
(Decca DL-4618)

Miss Smith Goes to Paris.. 5 - 3
(Decca DL-4640)

Lady Fingers.. 5 - 3
(Decca DL-4744)

Bright and Breezy... 5 - 3
(Decca DL-4799)

Roger **Smith**

In an episode of 77 Sunset Strip *titled 'Juke Box Caper," Roger Smith (as p.i. Jeff Spencer) is turned into a recording star by some hoods who control the town's jukebox racket. No such luck for Smith in real life: Recording stardom eluded him, but he had a pleasant enough voice, and his* Beach Romance *is a pleasantly romantic LP.*

Beach Romance.. 5 - 3
(Warner Bros. W/WS-1305, 1960)

Terry **Snyder**

Mr. Percussion... 5 - 3
(United Artists WWS-8500, 1961)

Unique Percussion [reissue of Mr. Percussion]...................................... 5 - 3
(United Artists WWS-8500, 1961)

Footlight Percussion .... 5 - 3
(United Artists WWS-8508)

Gentle Purr-cussion.. 5 - 3
(United Artists WWS-8521)

Imagine *Cabaret* with vocals by Connie Francis instead of Liza Minelli, and you'll have a fair idea of Elke Sommer's *Love in Any Language.* The German-born sex symbol was at the top of her cinema game when the LP came out, having scored in such pictures as *The Prize* (1963) with Paul Newman and *A Shot in the Dark* (1964), perhaps the best of the Pink Panther movies, with Peter Sellers. The album's hook was that Elke sang the 12 songs in a variety of languages: German, French, Spanish, Italian and, of course, English. A couple of these numbers, admittedly, push at the outer limits of the lounge classification, with their share of overwrought moments. But Ms. Sommer once replied to a fan letter from one of your authors with a wonderful photo and inscription all the way from Germany; she has been a favorite in these quarters ever since.

– JW

F o r e v e r

Frank **Socolow**

Sounds by Socolow .... 5 - 3
(Bethlehem BCP-47)

Elke **Sommer**

"This album should come as no surprise to anyone who has seen Elke Sommer on the screen. After all, with her looks and her figure and her acting talent, why shouldn't she also sing?

"The wonder of it is that she sings so well ... so very well.

"And in so many languages ....

"For Elke Sommer, singing has added a new facet of expression to an already imposing career in the arts. For the listener, her warm and definitely intimate way with a song is indeed a satisfying and pleasing experience."

[from the liner notes for *Love in Any Language*]

Love in Any Language .... 20 - 12
(MGM E/SE-4321, 1965)

South Sea Champion Drummers

Pahu Tahiti! .... 5 - 3
(Dot DLP-25297)

The **Stanley-Johnson** Orchestra

Have Harp, Can't Travel .... 5 - 3
(Liberty)

Cyril **Stapleton**

I Wish You Love .... 5 - 3
(Lion L-70056)
Paris After Dark .... 5 - 3
(MGM E-3206)
Italy After Dark .... 5 - 3
(MGM E-3302)

April **Stevens**

"April has introduced a new style of sexy singing to the music world, but her natural naivete prevents her from understanding the excitement over it. 'Everybody tells me my singing sounds sexy,'

220

she said. 'I really don't know why. I've been singing like that all my life, since I was seven.' But a comment from one of her many fan letters explains her appeal best. 'Your voice sounds as though you had a throat full of angora sweaters,' the letter reads. 'Other girl vocalists sing, but you actually talk to a guy and boy, the things you say!"

[from the liner notes for *Teach Me Tiger!*]

Torrid Tunes .... 100 - 60
    (Audio Lab AL-1534, 1959)
Teach Me Tiger! .... 75 - 45
    (Imperial LP-9055/12055, 1960)
Carousel Dreams .... 5 - 3
    (1978)

On CD: Carousel Dreams (USA Music Group, 1990); Sweet and Lovely: The Best of Nino Tempo and April Stevens (Varese Sarabande, 1996)

Morris **Stoloff**

Picnic [conducting the Columbia Picture Orchestra] .... 5 - 3
    (Decca DL-8320/78320)

Billy **Strange**

Mr. Guitar .... 5 - 3
    (Crescendo GNPS-97, 1964)
James Bond Theme and Others .... 5 - 3
    (Crescendo GNPS-2004, 1964)
Goldfinger .... 5 - 3
    (Crescendo GNPS-2006, 1965)
English Hits of '65 .... 5 - 3
    (Crescendo GNPS-2009, 1965)
Billy Strange Plays the Hits .... 5 - 3
    (Crescendo GNPS-2012, 1965)
Secret Agent File .... 5 - 3
    (Crescendo GNPS-2019, 1965)
In the Mexican Bag .... 5 - 3
    (Crescendo GNPS-2022, 1966)
Best of Billy Strange .... 5 - 3
    (Crescendo GNPS-2037, 1967)
James Bond Double Feature .... 5 - 3
    (Crescendo GNPS-2039)
Dyn-o-mite Guitar .... 5 - 3
    (Crescendo GNPS-2094)

The **Strings of Rio**

Yma **Sumac**

On CD: Voice of the Xtabay/Inca Taqui (The Right Stuff, 1996); Voice of the Xtabay/Inca Taqui (Capitol, 1987); Voice of the Xtabay (REV-OLA, 1995); Mambo (The Right Stuff, 1996); Mambo … and More! (REV-OLA, 1997); Legend of the Sun Virgin (Capitol, 1989); Legend of the Sun Virgin (The Right Stuff, 1996); Legend of the Jivaro (The Right Stuff, 1996); Fuego del Ande [mono and stereo versions] (The Right Stuff, 1996); Spell of Yma Sumac (Pair, 1987); Sampler Exotica (The Right Stuff, 1996); Amor Indio (Saludos Amigos, 1994); Yma Rocks! (ShamLys, 1998)

"Close your eyes and picture romance.

"Rio! A long curve of beach wearing a necklace of lights. A moonlit terrace and the scene of acacia trees. The warm caress of a tropical breeze. And in the distance, music – soft, languorous, seductive …

"Is it possible that while Epic was in Brazil recording the Strings of Rio in their own city, they also bottled the air, captured the breeze, recorded the scent? Or is it just your imagination?

"Whatever it is, take advantage of it. When the Strings of Rio cast their spell on a romantic evening, don't question it at all.

"Give in to it.

"Give in to it.

"Give in to it."

[from the Richard Maltby Jr. liner notes for *Love in a Latin Mood*]

Reinhold **Svensson**
(and His All-Star Jazz Sextet)

Terorotua and His Tahitians

Keith **Textor**

Bob **Thompson**

Bob Thompson's The Sound of Speed – an "Ultra Stereophonic Recording" – is a mild orchestral suite peppered with actual sounds of various vehicles. The song titles and their corresponding aural exciter: "Super Chief" (diesel train), "Midnight Sailing" (ocean liner), "La Vespa" (motor scooter), "Sub-Manhattan Blues" (subway train), "Three-Wheeler Waltz" (tricycle), "Count Down" (missile), "Star Fire" (jet plane), "Surrey Serenade" (horse & buggy), "Le Mans" (sports cars), "Streetcar Named Irving" (streetcar), "Sea-Spray" (speed boats) and "Early-Bird Whirly-Bird" (helicopter). – TC

Claude **Thornhill**

On CD: The Best of the Big Bands (Sony Special Procuts, 1991)

The **Three Suns**

This unusual package is designed to create excitement, stir emotions and kindle your imagination - so put the record on the turntable, turn up the volume, and control yourself.

Warning: Keep in a cool place.

[from Faith Whitehall's liner notes for Fever and Smoke *]*

"… Throughout their years of producing records, the Three Suns have established a reputation for palatable sounds. These sounds have been projected within the instrumentation of the group – accordian, guitar and organ – and, when desiring enhancement of the customary instruments, elaborated to include strings, brass and woodwinds. At times Al Nevins, producer of all of the Three Suns musical endeavors, has reached into the instrumental bag of tricks to uncover the exotic, the refreshing and the novel in sound. This imagination has placed the Three Suns on a pinnacle of musical taste. There has never been a bad record nor a bulky album. Thought and description have been blended with an understanding of what you would like to hear and the end result – success after success …

"Ray Bohr has excelled on the pipe organ and presented a new friend with the Three Suns. Twelve arrangements, delightfully planned by Sid Ramin, are coupled on one disc to provide an experience after dark for the most discriminating …"

[from Noel R. Kramer's liner notes for *Midnight for Two*]

Indispensable linchpins of lounge music, the Three Suns – guitarist Al Nevins, Morty Nevins (Al's brother) on accordian, and Artie Dunn (Al and Morty's cousin) on organ – crafted a ton of albums for RCA in the late '50s and early '60s. Their consistent, almost hypnotic, mellowness mask the fact that these guys were always experimenting – adding everything from vibraphone to mandolin at one time or another. Perhaps the apex of their noodling around with different sounds was *Midnight for Two,* whose marvelously goofy (and wildly phallic) cover art perfectly encapsulates the fog-bound romanticism of standards like "Stella By Starlight" and "I Don't Stand A Ghost of A Chance" shimmered through two organs, Hammond and pipe.

– JW

"... Incidentally, if you're not planning any afternoon love in the forseeable future, don't be discouraged. This album serves just as well for evening romance."

[from Dick Kleiner's liner notes for *Love in the Afternoon*]

"... In this new album, the Suns and all their friends depict some of the ways in which you can enjoy one of life's most delightful experiences – there's a lot of enjoyment to be had while luxuriating under the sun's rays. No matter where you may be right now ... no matter what you are doing ... it's a sun-drenched holiday of relaxation and pleasure whenever The Three Suns bring you FUN IN THE SUN."

[from the liner notes for *Fun in the Sun* (1961)]

Don **Tiare** Strings

Cal **Tjader**

Mas Ritmo Caliente .... 30 - 18
   (Fantasy 3262, 1957)
Latin for Lovers with Strings .... 30 - 18
   (Fantasy, 1958)
San Francisco Moods .... 30 - 18
   (Fantasy, 1958)
Cal Tjader Goes Latin .... 30 - 18
   (Fantasy F-3289/8030, 1959)
Latino .... 30 - 18
   (Fantasy F-8079, 1960)
Cal Tjader Plays, Mary Stalling Sings .... 30 - 18
   (Fantasy 3325, 1961)
Cal Tjader's Greatest Hits .... 15 - 9
   (Fantasy F-8366, 1965)
Latin for Dancers .... 20 - 12
   (Fantasy F-8374, 1966)
Last Night When We Were Young .... 20 - 12
   (Fantasy 3482/9482)
Amazonas .... 5 - 3
   (Fantasy F-9502, 1975)
Sounds Out Burt Bacharach .... 15 - 9
   (Skye SK-6, 1969)
In a Latin Bag .... 15 - 9
   (Verve V6-8419, 1961)
Several Shades of Jade .... 15 - 9
   (Verve V6-8507, 1963)
Sona Libre .... 15 - 9
   (Verve V6-8531, 1963)
Breeze from the East .... 15 - 9
   (Verve V6-8575, 1963)
Warm Wave .... 15 - 9
   (Verve V6-8585, 1964)
Soul Sauce .... 15 - 9
   (Verve V6-8614, 1965)
Hip Vibrations .... 15 - 9
   (Verve V6-8730, 1967)
The Best of Cal Tjader .... 15 - 9
   (Verve V6-8725, 1968)

On CD: Aqua Dulce (Fantasy, 1991); Latin + Jazz Equals (DCC); Sentimental Moods (Fantasy);
Black Orchid [Goes Latin and Quintet] (Original Jazz, 1993); Several Shades of Jade/Breeze from the
East (Polygram, 1997); Cal Tjader's Greatest Hits (Fantasy, 1995); Heat Wave (Concord Jazz, 1992);
Amazonas (Original Jazz Classics, 1995); Mambo With Tjader (Original Jazz Classics, 1992); Tjader
Plays Mambo (Original Jazz Classics, 1996); Latin Kick (Original Jazz Classics, 1991)

Mr. Mel

The ever-suave Mel Tormé.

Rhino Records

Mel **Tormé**

On CD: Live At The Maisonette (Rhino); Songs Of New York (Rhino); Collection (1942-1985) (Rhino); Smooth as Velvet (Laserlight); Mel Tormé Sings Fred Astaire (Bethlehem, 1995); A Vintage Year (Concord Jazz, 1992); Christmas Songs (Telarc, 1992); I've Got the World on a String (Pilz, 1994); A Tribute to Bing Crosby (Concord Jazz, 1994); Velvet & Brass (Concord Jazz, 1995); Mellow Moods (Pickwick, 1998); My Night to Dream: The Ballads Collection (Concord Jazz, 1997); Swingin' on the Moon (Delta, 1993); 16 Most Requested Songs (Columbia, 1993); The Best of Mel Tormé (Curb, 1993); Luck Be a Lady (Laserlight, 1993); Comin' Home Baby & Other Hits (Rhino Flashback, 1997); Standards by Mel Tormé (Ranwood, 1997); Mel Torme (Touch of Class, 1998); Magic of Mel Torme (Music Club, 1998); A&E Biography (Capitol, 1998); The Mel Tormé Collection, 1944-1985 [4 disc set] (Rhino, 1995); The London Sessions (DCC, 1992); With the Marty Paich Dek-Tette (Concord Jazz, 1988); Right Now! (Columbia-Legacy); That's All (Columbia, 1997); Tormé (Verve, 1992); Back in Town (Verve, 1991)

René **Touzet**,
His Piano and Orchestra

On CD: Dinner in Havana (BMG)

Georges **Tzipine**

"In motion pictures, and in the theater, 'background' music serves to heighten the mood of the moment and add to the charm of each situation. By the same token, smart hostesses find that delightful music, played softly, serves as an ideal background for dinner, for cocktails, or just for 'sitting around' ... when lulls in the coversation are pleasantly filled!"
[from the liner notes for *Dinner at Eight*]

When Capitol released Georges Tzipine's *Dinner at Eight* (played by his "salon orchestra") in early 1950, the golden age of lounge music still lay several years in the future. But it was discs like this one (despite the fact that it contains such unlikely selections as "Man on the Flying Trapeze" and "Polly Wolly Doodle," along with the more appropriate "Manhattan Serenade") that began emphasizing the whole notion of special background music for cocktails and conversation – an idea helped along, of course, by the extended-play and long-play records that replaced the one-song-per-side 78s. This was mood music, pure and simple, and as such was the precursor of the true lounge sound.

– JW

Art Van Damme is another tough call when it comes to lounge music. Certainly, he and his sidemen were accomplished jazz players. But, like Dave Brubeck, even at his jazziest there was always a pop-music sensibility wafting through. And the combination of accordian, vibraphone and guitar as lead instruments gives a mood-music feeling to just about all he does. We hope our hard-core jazz-fan pals won't mind the inclusion of some of Van Damme's work in this volume. It's only here because we really like it, and something like his hauntingly sensual version of "Laura" always throws us out among the stars.

– JW

(Capitol CC-146)

The **Ulterior Motive**
Orchestra

The Ulterior Motive Orchestra is not an actual group. The name was created to hang on a CD release of '60s-era spy music performed by two different collectives: David Lloyd and His London Orchestra and Johnny Pearson and His London Orchestra. Some of the cuts are James Bond titles, but they're not music from the original films; instead, these are compositions written by Warren Baker years before the movies appeared and inspired by the book titles.
– TC

On CD: S.P.Y.T.I.M.E. (Hi Fi Tradition, 1996)

Art **Van Damme**

"Winners of the Down Beat poll in 1952 and 1954, the Art Van Damme Quintet stands as one of the most inventive, musical and swinging combinations around. A group based on accordian, vibes, guitar, bass and drums could easily enough veer toward salon sounds and concepts, but the cloying sweetness of such ideas are a far cry from the breezy presentations of the Van Damme group. Their work is founded on lively interplay of musical ideas, on solid standard pieces and on a jazz base; therein lies the art of Van Damme, and therein also lies the entertainment of countless musicians and laymen alike …"
[from the liner notes for *The Art of Van Damme*]

New Sound of the Art Van Damme Septet 5-3
(Columbia CL-2192)
A Perfect Match 5-3
(Columbia CS-8813, 1962)
Septet 5-3
(Columbia CS-8992, 1964)
Invitation [with Singers Unlimited] 5-3
(MPS MC-22016, 1973)
Art Van Damme and Friends 5-3
(Pausa 7151, 1983)
Keep Going 5-3
(Pausa 7104)
Lover Man 5-3
(Pickwick 3009)
Sounds 5-3
(Columbia CL-544)

On CD: Van Damme Sound/Martini Time (Collectables, 1998)

Vardi and the Medallion Strings

The Sound of Hollywood 5-3
(Kapp Medallion ML-7513)
Wine, Women and Waltzes 5-3
(Kapp Medallion ML-7519)
Maggie's Theme 5-3
(Kapp Medallion ML-7527)

Various Artists

"Romance would be dull if it always came in the same mood. It's the variety of moods that keep romance interesting and the surprising changes that keep romance exciting ...

"We know that the romance is over once boredom creeps in so we have programmed this album to halt boredom dead in its tracks. Only the coldest heart can remain unmoved by a mixtures of cha cha chas, rumbas, merengues, mambos, tangos and sambas expecially when played by such experts in their field as Tito Puente, Neil Lewis, The Tico Orchestra, The Melino Orchestra and Pepe Rico...."

[from the liner notes for *Music for Romancing*]

"The Enchanted Tiki Room presents an entirely new kind of three dimensional entertainment called 'Audio-Animatronics,' an electronic wonder in a world of Walt Disney wonders. Tropical birds, flowers and tiki gods are heard in a fascinating musical comedy featuring 225 performers controlled by a 14 channel tape recorder which directs sound, lighting and movement. Audio-

[continued on page 236]

Inspired by the late '50s-early '60s ABC-TV show of the same name, which featured Gardner McKay as the laid-back owner of a South Seas boat-for-hire, *Adventures in Paradise* contained the theme song for that series along with selections by Roy Smeck ("The Wizard of the Strings"), Terorotua and His Tahitians, the Islanders, and the then-just-deceased Hawaiian vocalist Alfred Apaka.

– JW

Packages of smooth music that went home with buyers of new Zenith stereos, *Zenith Presents Around the World* and *Zenith Presents Curtain Time* hold up as first-class loungey collections. The former features the top-drawer easy-listening acts Ray Conniff, Michel Legrand, Andre Kostelanetz and Jerry Murad's Harmonicats; the latter, which subs romantic instrumental hits from Broadway and Hollywood for the white-guy world-music of the former, offers great stuff from Conniff, Don Costa, Skitch Henderson and the peerless trumpeter Bobby Hackett.

– JW

Columbia released tons of piano music in the late '50s and early '60s; the label's "Piano Moods" series featured discs from such big-name jazzers as Teddy Wilson and Erroll Garner along with now-overlooked ivory-ticklers like Nat Brandwynne and Herman Chittison. Piano Music for Parties *is a kind of sampler from several of these discs, and it includes a couple of selections from our own personal favorite jazz keyboardist, Jess Stacy, the guy who'll forever be remembered for his exquisite injection of creative subtlety into Benny Goodman's roaring live version of "Sing, Sing, Sing" at Goodman's 1938 Carnegie Hall concert.*
– JW

With easy-listening maestros Paul Weston, Percy Faith and Gordon Jenkins joining big-band leader Les Elgart, It's Unforgettable *was another of those "Zenith presents the thrilling world of STEREO" LPs that buyers got with the purchase of a new unit. And every tune on it, from Elgart's "Unforgettable" to Jenkins' "Stella by Starlight," was a bona fide romantic-pop evergreen.*
– JW

"Everyone has special songs that stir an immediate emotional response, a remembrance of moments passed – perhaps joyful, perhaps sentimental, but ones that are unmistakably reawakened each time those songs are heard. Most likely you will find such memory refreshers here, for It's Unforgettable *contains some of the most evocative songs ever written – songs that rouse the heart and delight the ear ..."*

[liner notes for *It's Unforgettable*]

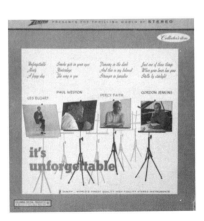

"From the golden treasury of master tapes in the ABC-Paramount archives comes this beautiful collection of tunes calculated to tranport you to Shangri-La, Tahiti, Samarkand, or wherever you consider Paradise to be. In this special selected dozen, you are certain to experience that personal emotion of bridging vast distances of time and space to your own version of the never-never land where you can indulge in daydreaming and mental beach-combing to your heart's content."

[from the Natt Hale liner notes for **Adventures in Paradise**]

With music composed by Leonard Roseman, this soundtrack to the 1962 George Cukor film about four women's sex lives (featuring, among other things, Efrem Zimbalist Jr. romancing ice-queen Jane Fonda) boasts plenty of fine mood music. It ends with two Roseman themes from James Dean movies: *East of Eden* and *Rebel Without a Cause*.

– JW, on **The Chapman Report**

Although it's unclear what the **The All-Star Color TV Review** had to do with color television, these two releases from the budget label Hollywood (which carried the Saturday Evening Post seal of "Recognized Value") had some pretty good names going for them, including those of Vic Damone, Lanny Ross, and Tutti Camarata's Orchestra.

– JW

Classified by disc (*Music By Candlelight, You and the Night and the Music, When the Lights are Low, Instrumentally Speaking*), **The Velvet Touch** "limited edition" set has a little something for everyone – especially lovers of the romantically offbeat. There's Doris Day's mini-epic version of Willie Nelson's "Night Life," Jim Nabors doing "The Story of a Starry Night," and Mark Lindsay's "Feel the Warm," along with the usual suspects (Johnny Mathis, Percy Faith, Ray Conniff, Andre Kostelanetz, Bobby Hackett) performing a combination of movie themes, evergreens and '60s pop.

– JW

animatronics has been developed over a period of years by Disney creative technicians. The music and song filled show stars the 'Four MacAudios,' Jose, Fritz, Pierre and Michael. In accents of Spanish, German, French and Irish they introduce the human-voiced birds who perform in a colorful South Seas setting. The waters of the Enchanted Fountain keep time to a primitive beat as beautiful singing orchids descend in elaborately carved canoes. Climax of the Enchanted Tiki Room show is the dramatic 'Hawaiian War Chant' featuring the primitive drums and chants of the tiki gods. It's an enchanting show!"

[from the liner notes for *Disneyland: The Enchanted Tiki Room & The Adventurous Jungle Cruise*]

Billy **Vaughn**

On CD: *Sail Along Silv'ry Moon (Bear Family, 1997); Melody of Love: The Best of Billy Vaughn (Varese Sarabande); Plays the Music You Remember (Pair, 1991); My Melody of Love (Special Music, 1991); Christmas Songs (Essex, 1992); Mundo Instrumental (Star, 1995); Christmas With Billy Vaughn (Eclipse, 1996); Best of Billy Vaughn and His Orchestra (Drive, 1993); Best of Billy Vaughn (Drive, 1987); Billy Vaughn and His Orchestra Play 22 of His Greatest Hits (Ranwood, 1988); String of Pearls: Billy Vaughn's Greatest Hits (Curb, 1992); Melody of Love: Best of Billy Vaughn (Varese Sarabande, 1994); Melody of Love: Best of Billy Vaughn (Ranwood, 1995); Christmas Classics (Chicago Music, 1995); Red Roses for a Blue Lady (MCA Special Products, 1996); La Paloma (Varese Sarabande, 1997)*

Ray **Ventura**
and His Orchestra

The **Video All-Stars**

Al **Viola**

Al Viola is one of several lounge-ish players that didn't ignore the Summer of Love. He shows up on some odd projects in the '70s, including playing guitar on Frank Zappa's Lumpy Gravy album. He never lost his mellow center, though. The Mello' as a Cello CD combines a 1979 round of Sinatra tributes with a 1980 session of easy-going instrumentals.
– TC

On CD: *Mello' as a Cello (Starline)*

Vital Organ

On CD: Murder at the Keyboard (Del-Fi, 1997)

Walter **Wanderley**

*On CD: Brazil's Greatest Hits (GNP Crescendo, 1990); Samba Swing (Scamp, 1996); Talkin'
Verve (Verve, 1998); Boss of the Bossa Nova [double disc] (1996)*

Guy **Warren**

Ben **Webster**

On CD: Warm Moods (Warner Bros., 1997)

Julius **Wechter**

You may have heard the percussion of Julius Wechter and not even known it. He appears on albums from a variety of rock groups, from the Monkees to the Tubes, and he also contributed multi-instrumental assistance to Leon Russell's The Wedding Album.
– TC

Ruth **Welcome**

"... Whatever she chooses to play, something happens as the melodic tones of her zither start to ring : The skyscrapers of Manhattan begin to dissolve... a martini becomes a glass of cognac ... and the Danube cannot be too far away, for suddenly, the room has been transformed into a romantic boulevard scene."

[from the liner notes for *At a Sidewalk Café*]

Lawrence **Welk**

On CD: The Best of Lawrence Welk (Vanguard, 1972); The Best of Lawrence Welk (Special Music 3022, 1982); The Best of Lawrence Welk (MCA 4044); 16 Most Requested Songs (Columbia, 1989); A Musical Anthology [boxed set] (Vanguard, 1992)

Mae **West**

On CD: I'm No Angel (Jasmine, 1996)

Paul **Weston**
(and His Orchestra)

"Music for a rainy night ... the pavements wet and shiny, the lights glistening through the darkness, the rain trickling down the windowpane in its time-honored tradition ... this is the time for quiet and relaxation, whether the rain is a quiet shower or the firm, steady downpour that lasts until the dim hours of morning. This is the time for coziness, for the quiet pleasure of reminiscence, for the songs of yesterday that are rich in melody and nos-

The West Coast Musical Director for Columbia Records, Paul Weston knew how to knit up a musical mood, and he knew just what moods he wanted on the records that bore his own name. *Music for a Rainy Night* is one of the direct forebears of all those Mystic Moods and other seduction-aid albums that would come along a decade or so later. For evidence, take a look at the front of the jacket, which is one of the best mood-music covers of all time. Liner notes to the contrary, the hungrily eager look on that model's face doesn't have much to do with either "coziness" or "the quiet pleasure of reminiscence," if you know what we mean.

– JW

"We have all had the experience of gathering around a fireplace on a crisp evening. At first the warmth and flickering flames have an almost hypnotic effect upon everyone. Nothing is heard but the crackling of flames … no word is spoken. And then music lends a gentle accompaniment to this perfect hour. Soft singing, perhaps … or the strumming of a guitar. Whatever the source, it is music that matches the fireside mood.

"Paul Weston offers just such music in this delightful album. Arranged for soft strings, whispering woodwinds and muted brass, each selection is as gentle as the curling smoke patterns, as lovely as the firelight reflected on the face of one beloved … (S)uch music is welcome everywhere from the most sophisticated penthouse apartment to the small cottage in a country town."

[from the liner notes for *Music for the Fireside*]

talgia, the songs that are music for a rainy night …"
[from the liner notes for *Music for a Rainy Night*]

On CD: The Original Music for Easy Listening (Corinthian, 1987); Easy Jazz (Corinthian, 1992); Music for Memories/Music for Dreaming (Capitol, 1992)

Jay **White**

Roger **Williams**

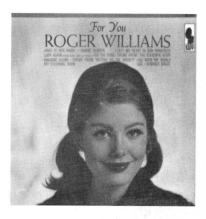

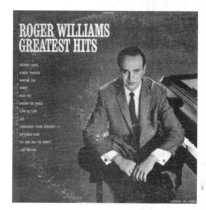

On CD: Easy Listening (Pair); Golden Christmas (Special Music); The Collection (Mobile Fidelity); The Best of the Beautiful (MCA, 1989); The Best of Roger Williams (MCA, 1989); Golden Hits, Vol. 2 (MCA, 1993); Great Piano Hits (Pair, 1995); Collection (Varese Sarabande, 1998); Nadia's Theme (MCA Special Procuts, 1990); Moments to Remember (MCApecial Products, 1993); Plays More Golden Songs of Love (MCA Special Products, 1995); Plays the Songs of Love (MCA Special Products, 1995); Greatest Movie Themes (Hip-O, 1996); Christmas Time (MCA Special Products, 1995); Greatest Hits (MCA); The Greatest Popular Pianist: The Artist's Choice [double disc] (MCA, 1992)

Murry **Wilson**

"This album is a first! Because it features Murry Wilson – songwriter!
   "Until this time, the public has known Murry Wilson only as the father and initial personal manager-recording director of the world famous Beach Boys. The man who rocketed them into a phenomenal career.
   "Now it's Murry Wilson's turn! You will hear a side of Murry that only his family and close friends are aware of – the songwriter with a flair for melodic structure! And you'll also hear a fantastic mixture of sounds uncommon to most recordings! …"
   [from the liner notes for *The Many Moods of Murry Wilson*]

Nancy **Wilson**

Nancy Wilson remained a seminal songstress well into the '90s. At the turn of that decade, Johnny Mercer's widow discovered some lost lyrics written by her Cole Porter-esque late husband. She asked Barry Manilow – king of modern-day schmaltzy standards – to write music for them

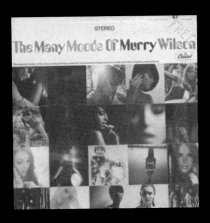

Forget the surfer girls and go-go chicks on the cover (and forget the exclamation marks in the liner copy). What this album is about is the dour-looking middle-aged guy with the pipe and old-fart glasses in the black and white wallet-size on the back of the package. Was he sadistic ogre or sensitive misunderstood artist? The father of Beach Boys Brian, Dennis and Carl has been painted as both, and perhaps, at different times, he was both. But we have *The Many Moods of Murry Wilson* ("Conceived and Produced by Murry Wilson") to show us that he had a pretty good ear for loungey sounds. Here, he can sound a little like the Three Suns (in "Betty's Waltz," co-written with wife

Love life

The famous Nancy Wilson pout.

Rhino Records

and record them. Manilow accepted and turned to Wilson to provide the lungs. The result – 1991's With My Lover Beside Me – *was charming and surprisingly well-done.*
– TC

Audree) or something like the Kostelanetz orchestra (on "Islands in the Sky," written by Rick Henn, the leader of the Sunrays – which was the band Murry managed after the Beach Boys gave him the haurachi to the backside). Songwriters also represented here, in addition to Murry, include then 40-year-old plumber Eck Kynor and mood-music great Don Ralke, of *But You've Never Heard Gershwin With Bongos* and *Mystic Moods Orchestra* fame. Ralke also arranged and conducted the sessions for the Murry Wilson album, which goes a long way toward explaining why the tunes still sound so good.

– JW

The two biggest TV-drama genres of the late '50 and early '60s were western and private-eye. Viewers got a combo order with *Shotgun Slade* (syndicated, 1959-61), featuring two-fisted Scott Brady as an old-West hardboiled detective who packed a double-barrelled weapon: 12-gauge shotgun on the bottom, .32 caliber rifle on the top. Composer Gerald Fried (*Wagon Train, M-Squad*) went for the double-barrelled approach in his music, too, combining the pastoral and other elements of western theme music with jazz in such cuts as "Gently" and "Rolling Home," and utilizing banjos and a snatch of "My Darling Clementine" in one called "Them Swingin' Doors." The predominant music, however, was straight TV jazz, which is why you'll find the album in this book.

– JW

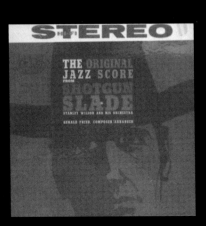

On CD: Yesterday's Love Songs, Today's Blues (Blue Note, 1991); Lush Life (Blue Note, 1995); Welcome to My Love (Capitol, 1995); Best of Nancy Wilson (Capitol); Ballads, Blues and Big Bands: The Best of Nancy Wilson (Capitol, 1996); The Best of Nancy Wilson: Jazz and Blues (Capitol, 1996); Swingin's Mutual [with George Shearing] (Capitol, 1992); But Beautiful (Capitol, 1990); Nancy Now! (Columbia, 1989); With My Lover Beside Me (Columbia, 1991)

Stanley **Wilson**
(and His Orchestra)

"Because the creators of 'Shotgun Slade' determined to bridge the chasm of time between normal western sagas of the 19th century and the materful, worldly 'private eye' of the 20th centry, background music, too, had to merge music from almost a 100-year period into mood melody for the series ..."
    [from the liner notes for *The Original Jazz Score From Shotgun Slade*]

Kai **Winding**

Hugo **Winterhalter**

On CD: The Eyes of Love (Good Music); Christmas Music (Essex, 1992); Two Sides of Winterhalter (RCA, 1996); The Best of Easy Listening (Richmond, 1996); 16 Beautiful Hits (Deluxe, 1994)

George **Wright**

On CD: At the Mighty Wurlitzer (Legacy, 1994)

Yazz Band

[See Richards, Emil]

Si **Zenter**
(and His Orchestra)

On CD: Si Zenter and His Orchestra Alive in Las Vegas (Klavier, 1992); Road Band (Klavier, 1996); Plays Frank Sinatra (Klavier, 1998)

CD Collections

I t doesn't take a lot of courage or adventurousness to appreciate Space-Age Pop. A sense of humor helps, as do a reckless spirit and a cocktail shaker. Is it high art? Timeless culture? Is it worthy of serious consideration? If you're reflecting about such matters, we suggest you accompany your ruminations with recordings by Harry Chapin. Harry addressed the really big questions. He may provide the guidance you seek. Cocktail Mix is not for you.

On the other hand, if you long for the days when smokers had rights and exercised them freely – in public; when alcohol was imbided without finger-wagging by the FDA; before fat-free became a national fixation – in short, for the days when people enjoyed themselves without guilt – then Cocktail Mix is just the tonic.

Crank up the hi-fi, kick off your shoes, light up, knock back a few, have fun – and accept the consequences. You're an adult. Ultimately, that's who this music is for – grown-ups. Responsible people in irresponsible moods. Welcome aboard to the last train to Squaresville."

[from Irwin Chusid's liner notes for *Bachelor's Guide to the Galaxy*, Vol. 1 of Rhino's three-CD collection, *Cocktail Mix*]

Incredibly Strange Music, Vol. 1
   (Asphodel-Caroline 0950, 1993)
Incredibly Strange Music, Vol. 2
   (Asphodel-Re/Search 0951, 1995)
Bachelor in Paradise: MGM Film Music
[Liberace, Desi Arnaz, Henry Mancini, Esquivel, Les Baxter,
Mel Torme, Ann-Margret, Ferrante and Teicher, etc.]
   (Atlantic-Rhino, 1996)
James Bond: 25 Years of 007
   (Bainbridge 2074 [LP was BT-6274], 1988)
Let It Snow! Cuddly Christmas Classics From Capitol
[Bing Crosby, Julie London, Dean Martin, Al Martino,
Kay Starr, Lena Horne, Lou Rawls, Peggy Lee, etc.]
   (Capitol C2-99692, 1992)
Far Away Places: Capitol Sings Around the World
[Billy May, Andre Previn, Pete Rugolo,
Alvino Rey, Nelson Riddle]
   (Capitol, 1994)
Route 66: Capitol Sings Coast to Coast
[with Peggy Lee, Dean Martin, Dinah Shore, Kay Starr,
Nancy Wilson, Tony Bennett, Ella Fitzgerald, etc.]
   (Capitol, 1994)
Hooray for Love: Great Gentlemen of Song, Vol. 1
[features Billy May, Dean Elliott, Bobby Hammack,
Duke Ellington, Nelson Riddle, and more]
   (Capitol 31774, 1995)
Bachelor Pad Royale
[18 tracks including Julie London, Martin Denny,

Nelson Riddle, Jimmie Haskell, etc.]
   (Capitol 35177, 1996)
Ultra-Lounge, Vol. 1: Mondo Exotica
   (Capitol, 1996)
Ultra-Lounge, Vol. 2: Mambo Fever
   (Capitol, 1996)
Ultra-Lounge, Vol. 3: Space Capades
   (Capitol, 1996)
Ultra-Lounge, Vol. 4: Bachelor Pad Royale
   (Capitol, 1996)
Ultra-Lounge, Vol. 5: Wild, Cool and Swingin'
   (Capitol, 1996)
Ultra-Lounge, Vol. 6: Rhapsodesia
   (Capitol, 1996)
Ultra-Lounge, Vol. 7: The Crime Scene
   (Capitol, 1996)
Ultra-Lounge, Vol. 8: Cocktail Capers
   (Capitol, 1996)
Ultra-Lounge, Vol. 9: Cha-Cha de Amor
   (Capitol, 1996)
Ultra-Lounge, Vol. 10: A Bachelor in Paris
   (Capitol, 1996)
Ultra-Lounge, Vol. 11: Organs in Orbit
   (Capitol, 1996)
Ultra-Lounge, Vol. 12: Saxophobia
   (Capitol, 1996)
Ultra-Lounge, Vol. 13: TV Town
   (Capitol, 1997)

Ultra-Lounge, Vol. 14: Bossa Novaville
(Capitol, 1997)

Ultra-Lounge, Vol. 15: Wild, Cool and Swingin' Too!
(Capitol, 1997)

Ultra-Lounge, Vol. 16: Mondo Hollywood
(Capitol, 1997)

Ultra-Lounge, Vol. 17: Bongoland
(Capitol, 1997)

Ultra-Lounge, Vol. 18: Bottoms-Up!
(Capitol, 1997)

Ultra-Lounge Fuzzy Sampler
(Capitol, 1997)

On the Rocks, Part One
(Capitol)

On the Rocks, Part Two
(Capitol)

Christmas Cocktails, Part 1
(Capitol, 1996)

Christmas Cocktails, Part 2
(Capitol, 1997)

Instrumental Themes for Young Lovers
(Columbia-Legacy, 1997)

Livin' Lounge: The Fabulous Sounds of Now!
[Love Jones, Lounge Lizards, Buster Poindexter]
(Continuum, 1995)

Secret Agent File
[credits include Leon Russell on synths, Les Baxter
on synths and arranger, Glen Campbell on guitar, TV
themes and Bond-style tunes]
(Crescendo GNPD-2166)

All-Time Great Instrumental Hits, Vol. 1
[12 tracks, including Les Baxter, Ferrante and
Teicher, Les Paul, Don Costa, etc.]
(Curb-Capitol, 1990)

Music for a Bachelor's Den, Vol. 1: Music for a
Bachelor's Den in Hi-Fi
[Terry Snyder, David Rose, Jackie Gleason, Arthur
Lyman, George Shearing, Martin Denny, etc.]
(DCC Compact Classics, 1995)

Music for a Bachelor's Den, Vol. 2: Exotica
(DCC Compact Classics, 1995)

Music for a Bachelor's Den, Vol. 3: Latin Rhythms in
Hi-Fi
(DCC Compact Classics, 1995)

Music for a Bachelor's Den, Vol. 4:
Easy Rhythms for Your Cocktail Hour
(DCC Compact Classics, 1995)

Music for a Bachelor's Den, Vol. 5:
The Best of the Arthur Lyman Group
(DCC Compact Classics, 1995)

Music for a Bachelor's Den, Vol. 6:
More of the Best of the Arthur Lyman Group
(DCC Compact Classics, 1995)

Music for a Bachelor's Den, Vol. 7:
Sex Kittens in Hi-Fi: The Blondes
(DCC Compact Classics, 1995)

Music for a Bachelor's Den, Vol. 8:
Sex Kittens in Hi-Fi: The Brunettes
(DCC Compact Classics, 1995)

Shots in the Dark [Henry Mancini tribute]
(Del-Fi/Donna DOCD-2113, 1996)

Deep in the Jungle
[with Preston Epps, Eden Ahbez, etc.]
(Del-Fi)

Great American Songwriters: Cole Porter
[Sinatra, Clooney, etc.]
(Delta, 1994)

In-Flight Entertainment
(Deram [Germany])

Espresso
[*Espresso* is the sequel to In-Flight Entertainment,
produced by the Karminsky Experience]
(Deram [Germany])

Journey to the Ancient City
[tribute to Korla Pandit]
(Dionysus, 1996)

The Mambo Kings [soundtrack]
(Elektra, 1992)

Cocktail Companion
[Southern Culture on the Skids, Man or Astroman?, etc.]
(Estrus)

Mission Accomplished: Themes for Spies
[from Lalo Schifrin to Jan Hammer]
(Hip-O, 1996)

Cigar Classics, Vol. 4: Smokin' Lounge
(Hip-O/Universal, 1997)

Swingers [soundtrack]
(Hollywood, 1996)

The scene is a foreboding, exotic bar waiting to deal with Dr. No or the one-armed man.

[from Stacey Elizabeth Toon's review of Secret Agent S.O.U.N.D.S. *in* Cheese Ball *]*

Austin Powers: International Man of Mystery [soundtrack]

(Hollywood, 1997)

Lounge-a-Palooza

[a kind of tribute disc to lounge featuring Combustible Edison with Esquivel, Steve Lawrence and Eydie Gorme (doing "Black Hole Sun"), Pizzicato Five, Edwyn Collins, even Glen Campbell with Michelle Shocked and Freddy Fender ("Wichita Lineman")]

(Hollywood 62072, 1997)

Swingin' Cheese: Croon Tunes and Kitscherama

[Ray Conniff, Sergio Mendes, etc.]

(Irma 488689, 1997)

Those Wonderful Instrumentals

[Percy Faith, Ferrante and Teicher, Lawrence Welk, Arthur Lyman, Les Baxter, Don Costa and more]

(K-Tel 3091-2, 1993)

Lounge Legends

[Paul Anka, Sammy Davis Jr., Englebert Humperdink]

(K-Tel, 1996)

Bachelor's Little Black Book

(LaserLight, 1996)

Bachelor in Paradise [three discs]

[Tito Puente, Xavier Cugat, Nelson Riddle, Andre Previn, Perez Prado, etc.]

(LaserLight, 1996)

Rare Mancini: A Tribute to Henry Mancini

[features Anita Kerr Singers, Eartha Kitt, Mancini, Rod McKuen, etc.]

(LaserLight 12430)

Secret Agent S.O.U.N.D.S.

[features Combustible Edison]

(Mai Tai, 1995)

Bachelor Pad Christmas

[David Rose, Connie Francis, Mel Torme, etc.]

(PolyGram, 1996)

Bachelor Pad Pleasures

[Esquivel, David Rose, Sergio Mendes, Kai Winding, Sammy Davis Jr., etc.]

(PolyGram, 1996)

Lounge Music Goes Latin

[Esquivel, Xavier Cugat, Sergio Mendes, Cal Tjader, Edmundo Ros, etc.]

(PolyGram, 1996)

Talkin' Verve … With a Twist

[lounge stuff from Quincy Jones, Stan Getz, Sammy Davis Jr., Mel Torme, Xavier Cugat and more … even Those Fantabulous Strings … has Getz doing a Bond-like reading of CSN's "Marrakesh Express"!]

(Polygram 537914, 1997)

Best of the Tropical Series

[Perez Prado, Noro Morales, Tito Rodriguez, Tito Puente]

(RCA, 1992)

Best of the Mambo

[Beny More, Noro Morales, Perez Prado, both Titos, Maynard Ferguson]

(RCA, 1992)

The History of Space Age Pop, Vol. 1: Melodies and Mischief

(RCA/Advance, 1995)

The History of Space Age Pop, Vol. 2: Mallets in Wonderland

(RCA/Advance, 1995)

The History of Space Age Pop, Vol. 3: The Stereo Action Dimension

(RCA/Advance, 1995)

Voices of Living Stereo, Vol. 1

(RCA, 1996)

Voices of Living Stereo, Vol. 2

[Henri Rene, Arthur Fiedler, etc.]

(RCA, 1996)

Another Crazy Cocktail Party

(RCA, 1997)

Mambo Mania! The Kings and Queens of Mambo

[features things like Desi Arnaz singing "Un Poquito de Tu Amor" with a small percussive combo rather than a band, plus Prado, More, the Titos, Xavier, Machito, etc.]

(Rhino, 1995)

Santamental Journey: Pop Vocal Christmas Classics

(Rhino, 1995)

Cocktail Mix, Vol. 1: Bachelor's Guide to the Galaxy

(Rhino, 1995)

Cocktail Mix, Vol. 2: Martini Madness

(Rhino, 1996)

Early modern purveyors of the style today such as Buster Poindexter, Love Jones are in good company with the likes of scenesters The Wonderful World of Joey and Everlounge.

[from Stacey Elizabeth Toon's review of Livin' Lounge *in* Cheese Ball]

Cocktail Mix, Vol. 3: Swingin' Singles
  (Rhino, 1996)
Cocktail Mix, Vol. 4: Soundtracks With a Twist!
  (Rhino, 1996)
Crime Jazz: Music in the First Degree
  (Rhino, 1997)
Crime Jazz: Music in the Second Degree
  (Rhino, 1997)
Jackpot! The Las Vegas Story
[Vic Damone, Wayne Newton,
Louis Prima, Sammy Davis Jr.,
Dean Martin, Eartha Kitt,
Mel Tormé, Liberace, etc.]
  (Rhino, 1997)
Instrumental Favorites: Exotic Moods
  (Rhino)
Instrumental Favorites: Latin Rhythms
  (Rhino)
Frolic Diner Series
  (Romulan [Germany])
The Sound Spectrum
  (Romunlan [Germany])
Hi-Fi Daze/Cocktail Nights
[combo of *In a Cocktail Mood* and
Music for the Jet Set]
  (Rykodisc, 1997)
In a Cocktail Mood
  (Rykodisc, 1997)
Music for the Jet Set
  (Rykodisc, 1997)
Shaken, Not Stirred
  (Rykodisc, 1997)
The Sound Gallery, Vol. 1
  (Scamp, 1996)
The Sound Gallery, Vol. 2
  (Scamp, 1996)
The Easy Project: 20 Loungecore Favorites
  (Sequel)
The Sound Spectrum
  (Sequel)
20 Loungecore Favorites
  (Sequel)

Exotic Excursion
[features Frank Capp, John Williams,
Robert Drasnin]
  (Simitar 1132, 1996)

Arranger & composer titles

From This Moment On: The Songs of Cole Porter
  (Smithsonian, 1993)
More Songs for Sleepless Nights
[odd collection with Percy Faith, Bryan Ferry,
Marty Paich, Sinead O'Connor and more]
  (Sony 57682, 1993)
Musical Meals: Cocktail Hour
  (Sony, 1994)
Braziliza!
[featuring Sergio Mendes, Baden Powell,
Jorge Ben, Edu Lobo, the Tambia Trio and more]
  (Talkin' Loud, 1994)
Batmania: Songs Inspired by the
"Batman" TV Series
[Neal Hefti's show theme, Adam West's "Miranda,"
the theme played by Al Hirt and Dave Allan, songs
by Burgess Meredith and Frank Gorshin, etc.]
  (Varese 5821, 1997)
Nova Bossa: Red Hot on Verve
[Getz/Gilbertos' "Girl From Ipanema,"
Walter Wanderley, Edu Lobo, Sergio Mendes]
  (Verve, 1996)
This Is Easy
[double-disc with '60s pop and film/TV themes,
odd stuff, from Jose Feliciano's "Light My Fire" to
Tijuana Brass "A Taste of Honey,"
listed producers include Sergio Mendes,
Herb Alpert, Hal David and Burt Bacharach]
  (Virgin 80, 1996)
Instrumental Moods
  (Virgin, 1998)
The KBZ 200: The Exotic Trilogy, Vol. 1
[Seven different versions of three classic songs:
"Caravan," "Taboo" and "Quiet Village" (21 tracks
in all)]

L   o   u   n   g   e

259

Goodnight, Mother

How Plato missed the boat on Edie Hart.

By John Wooley

If you remember your humanities classes, you may recall that Plato refused to allow any writers into his republic, that perfect society he talked about building. His reason, as we remember it, was that writers were just too far removed from the ideal. Plato believed that there was an ideal version of everything – a bowl, a chair, a harp, whatever – and the best any of us on earth could do was create something that approached that ideal, because our humanness made it impossible for us to do it *exactly* like the ideal, which existed somewhere out there in heaven. And the reason Plato didn't want any writers cluttering up his utopian community was that the best writers could do was write about the non-ideal thing that was crafted by human hands. Writers were, in other words, not just once but twice removed from the ideal.

If Plato's still hanging around somewhere out in the ether, and if he's still working on this thing, we humbly suggest that he relax his restrictions enough to let at least one writer in. And our nomination is writer-producer-director Blake Edwards. Not because he created some great movies (including *Days of Wine and Roses*, *Breakfast at Tiffany's*, and our own personal favorite, *A Shot on the Dark*), but because he managed to skip past both human levels and create, simply, the ideal lounge.

It was called Mother's. Edwards created it for his television series *Peter Gunn*. And while Mother's lasted a scant three years, undergoing a name change during its final year, it became nothing less than the template, the ultimate paradigm, of the perfect lounge. It may not have existed as a place where we could actually go, except in the single black-and-white dimension of our television sets, but there's fact and there's reality, and this place was real. It was as real as the smoke and the subdued conversation that broke and drifted like dust motes whenever singer Edie Hart strolled languidly up to the big microphone, knowingly murmuring lyrics about broken romances and brief and breezy affairs over pulsating vibraphone riffs, whispering brushes on drumheads, and piano chords subtly touched off by a cat named Emmett.

Here are the facts: Mother's was the place where a television p.i. named Peter Gunn (played to perfection by a middle-aged actor named Craig Stevens) spent a lot of his time – interviewing people in trouble, catching up with his friend Lieutenant Jacoby (Herschel Bernardi), or simply having a smoke and a drink as he watched his main squeeze, Edie (Lola Albright, who made the character every lounge fan's fever dream), warble a number or two. *Peter Gunn* debuted over NBC-TV in September of 1958, helping to kick off a TV private-eye craze. It jumped to ABC-TV two years later, expiring in 1961. By the time the cameras stopped rolling, the series had gone through two different Mothers. Hope Emerson, the physically imposing, hatchet-faced character actress, was the first. She died, at the age of 63, in 1960, and the equally grizzled Minerva Urecal – fondly remembered by horror fans for her weird matriarchal roles in Monogram's Bela Lugosi pictures – stepped in, fresh from having played the title role in the short-lived TV series *Tugboat Annie*.

Both Mothers presided over the same joint. It was a waterfront bar, but not the kind where Popeye-style drunks muttered old sea stories and shifty-eyed first mates keelhauled unwary drunks. It was instead a classy place, as hip and urbane as Gunn himself. It was a place where, with apologies to *Cheers*, everybody knew your game, and the regulars on both sides of the bar kept their own counsel.

Mother's had a rear door that led out to a kind of pier, jutting out onto the waterfront. It was a convenient place for Pete and Edie to meet, a private place where Edie could tell Pete what a drag it was to be in love with him, where they could throw their cigarettes over the railing and listen to them sizzle as they hit the water, where they could kiss and clench until Emmett (Bill Chadney) – who probably loved Edie himself in his own lonely jazzcat way – came out the door to get Edie for her next number.

In one memorable episode, Mother's was blown up by a criminal mastermind miffed at both Pete and Mother, an act that very nearly caused Pete to lose his deep and substantial cool. But the club – like Pete's detached savoir faire – had been rebuilt by the next episode, and it persevered from then on, ending its short but wonderful life as Edie's, owned by the singer and presided over by a majordomo named Leslie (James Lamphier), a big sensitive lug right out of a Raymond Chandler novel. The familiar neon "Mother's" that glowed perpendicularly from the side of the place became the quieter, subtler, "Edie's," and the show went on, at least for a little while longer.

Those are the facts. The impressions, however, are just as important. For many of us – especially those who got their first taste of the lounge lifestyle from the series – the mention of Mother's brings up the lingering image of Gunn, sharkskin suit and skinny tie, slipping up behind Mother and running a finger down her back, surprising her.

"Don't you have a home?" she rasps.

"Maid's night out," he returns.

There's a fleeting frozen moment of Emmett, his hands together over the keyboard as though he's in prayer, just before the fingers form a chord. And there's Edie, smiling as she sees Pete walk in. She's singing about a place called Dreamsville, knowing that, sooner or later, the two of them will be there.

And really, isn't this whole thing about Dreamsville? Isn't Dreamsville where the music, the true lounge music, takes us? And isn't it where we want to go?

Your Dreamsville may be a slightly different destination, with different faces, different dreams. But if it all didn't begin at Mother's, it came together there, where wry coolness met hardboiled attitude, where jazz hipsters and square popsters moved a couple of steps toward each other, where Edie even now sings, that curious, sensuous, half-smile on her lips, as Pete shushes Mother and nods approvingly from his booth, and the music – sweet, seductive, and a little sad – plays on, floating through the forever night, creating dreams that even Plato could love.

Pete loved Edie:

he knew where

to find her.

Edie loved Pete:

he always

went back.

Mark Van S.

Let's have a Nightcap

In Seattle, the word grunge doesn't work anymore as a method of describing the music scene. One local lounge-jazz outfit, the Nightcaps, are making a name and a living playing a juked-up version of lounge-style jazz that earns them plenty of cool gigs and style points in the cool department. The Nightcaps are, from left, percussionist John Broeckel, singer Theresa Hannam, drummer Dan Cunneen, guitarist Garth Brandenburg and bass player Robert Fucci.

Into
THE
Night

Seattle's Nightcaps give hope – and a whole lot of hip – to a new generation of lounge lizards. By Mark Brown

What a tragedy it is when a singer dies and the song with it.

Like the ancient secrets on a *seanachaoi's* lips, when they go they're pretty much gone. Whole movements of music have surely run the course of obscurity, antiquity and extinction with a final, barely audible dying note. How lonely, how sad the last sound must be.

Preservation of a style is, I guess, a selfish thing. We'll never be without Sinatra because somebody somewhere must hoard her stacks of Capitol recordings, must keep his Frank file up to date. And the idiosyncrasies of musicians? What makes them revere particular sounds of a genre, different artists within a style? What exactly *is* the difference between Hank Williams and Hank Williams Jr.? I leave it to the artists to figure out. Hell, they're the ones on the front line.

I went to see Seattle's Nightcaps to beg a question: Does a '90s club act plays '60s lounge-style music in order to preserve it? Would a modern-day lounge act evoke a latter-day lounge mood? Could I, by watching the Nightcaps and sipping a cold cocktail beyond the midnight hour, get a taste of that sound, that feeling that we now call lounge?

IT'S A WARM SATURDAY NIGHT in downtown Seattle. Warm as it gets, anyway. Inside the 700 Club, it's starting to get hot. Cigarettes have clouded the air, and the full house wears a sheen. Half-full and nearly empty beer glasses dot mix-and-match tables. There's a low hum, of small talk and laughter.

After a weekful of espresso and ale, what I crave is a stiff drink. A waitress makes her way over. We order and inquire about tonight's live entertainment.

"The band's all set," she says. "They're just waiting on Theresa."

So we sit back and wait. The 700 Club looks like the real thing, from its freshly raw riveting to its fashionably gamy doorman. Soon, the waitress returns with four shimmering cocktails. We pay up and sip and try without success to talk over the crowd, the band, and the pool hall one floor below. It feels better to just sit and absorb.

The Nightcaps – which at the moment is five guys in dark, smart suits – are deep into that non-melodic mating call, the resonant ritual of a band tuning up. Other than the suits, their looks vary. Tall guy on bongos, cute guy on bass, left-handed guitar player, Asian saxman. I can't make out the drummer through all the suitcoats, skinny ties and cymbals. All in all, they look very together, in an apart kind of way.

Things pick up when Nightcap singer Theresa Hannam walks in and takes the stage. The air is charged. The chatter quickens, the lights change colors, and the garbled tuning noise fades. The Nightcaps are assembled. There's going to be music.

I like Hannam right off. She's what you picture in a lounge singer. She's built solid but well off the ground, with fairly tight curls and a sentimental smile. She's wearing a spaghetti-strap gown and the way it falls off her shoulders and back reminds me of Ruth Roman in *Strangers on a Train.* Or an Apollo rocket, still strapped into the launchpad. She moves and gestures with poise and commands a working-class respect, which I'd give anyone who just got off work and was about to perform for three hours. She looks like she can handle it.

The band kicks in, but I still don't know what to expect. Somebody tells you you're going to see a lounge act … that can go a lot of ways. With a woman out front, they could veer on the torch side. But six members strong they could generate a pulse, too. They're young, so they know who Combustible Edison is. I'm semiconscious of all this but wedded to none of it.

As I suck the gin from a toothpicked Spanish olive, I'm sucked into the sound of the Nightcaps, led by the voice of Theresa Hannam, alternately breathy and cheeky, brusk and eternal. The lyrics drip off her tongue engagingly, ooze out of her passionately. Behind this mike and in front of this band, she's not just in her element, she's writing a new table.

Between songs, she plays easily to the crowd. "Say hello to Stephanie," Theresa says over the mike, "she'll be your waitress tonight. And a mighty good-lookin' one at that."

I go to the bar and order another Sapphire martini. While it's shaking, I look back to the stage and, through the smoky haze, see what it is that I like about the Nightcaps. Their sound is revved. It's lounge because you can sulk to it, but it's too tight to allow for sloppiness. They're right on, and somewhere, in that neverwhere between jazz and juke, they're stroking a nerve. And that voice is the nerve ending.

"I KNEW WE HAD TO HAVE a powerful presence up front," drummer and Nightcaps founder Dan Cunneen says. "Someone who could sing on key, but someone kind of sassy and diva-esque. Theresa's a rocker. We met when I was playing in a punk band and she was into '80s metal. But we both always enjoyed jazz.

"So when we started the Nightcaps, we were certainly trying to emulate a lounge style, but infuse a rock 'n' roll element into it."

Rock they do. A lot of their songs *are* soft, jazzy numbers geared toward Hannam's grouty throat, a slow-pulsed bassline, punctuated with moody horn riffs. But many of them run at a faster, heavier clip, charged by more modern beats. It isn't altogether unseemly that a '90s lounge music act would have a harder edge than a '60s one. After three decades of rock 'n' roll, it seems fitting.

Mark Van S.

The voice

Theresa Hannam, the Nightcaps' sultry, swingin' lead singer.

"Lounge is an umbrella term for a lot of stuff that came out in the '60s, and '50s," Day says. "It could be Martin Denny's *Exotica*, or it could be Dean Martin or Bobby Darin, who were just pop singers. I guess easy listening was the term that grew out of it, and the market was my grandparents. A lot of the parents of people my age weren't into lounge, they were into Led Zeppelin."

IT ISN'T "STAIRWAY TO HEAVEN" that's got a rather ripe group of women dancing in the corner of the 700 Club. It's Elvis Presley's "Burning Love," sung swingingly by Hannam to a roundhouse verve from her Nightcaps. They use it to close the first set. The crowd's juiced: they applaud enthusiastically and head to the bar for refills.

"I used to impersonate Elvis as a little kid," Hannam says. Then she took five years of voice lessons and began studying singers as a passion, admiring such divas as Chris Connor and Betty Carter. "The first one I really loved was Billie Holiday. I know it sounds cliched. I was 17 or 18 then. Of course, I'd heard Ella Fitzgerald, but I liked Holiday because she emoted so much better. You *believed* what she was singing. When Ella sang a depressed song, I never thought she was depressed."

My own interest in music didn't begin with Nancy Sinatra or Julie London – she was Dixie on *Emergency* by the time I caught her act – so to imagine a Vegas lounge diva in her prime I'd have to ad lib. I'd have to create a club scene of my own, a satin-covered scenario redolent of perfect hair and butane. Seated in back, where the drinks are watery but no less expensive, I can measure the crowd, survey the spenders as they palm big tips and get prime tables.

I can picture Joey Bishop making an entrance in a tuxedo blacker than oil, with a saucy broad towering four inches over him. They take a table next to Bo Belinsky and Tina Louise. Vegas is indeed L.A.'s playpen. Through a haze of hope and with the glaze of cheap bourbon and soda on my tongue, I envision mobsters, senators, boxers and big-leaguers all filing in to catch the hottest act in town.

I look around the 700 Club. It looks like a distressed Vegas after-hours walkup. A few pressed suits, people sharing ear whispers between smokes of Camels and cloves and sips from well-fingered vessels. At various points around the room, little gargoyle statuettes are positioned. The one in front of me has a cigar in its mouth. I'm starting to get it.

And the Nightcaps are starting their second set. It begins with a slow number, very jazzy, almost bluesy, like the light that Theresa Hannam's bathed in. She tilts her head back and words pop out like soap bubbles, each coated in silken, translucent weightlessness. She pitches her words, like a picador, and we give in to them. The music wafts through the room, seemingly *out* of it, into the warmly pleasant Seattle night.

"I want to purvey to the audience tonally, if not lyrically," Hannam says. "Even if they can't hear the words, they can still get an emotion. I want to convey some feeling, whether it's the embittered feeling of love lost, a completely sassy lyric, or a very depressing one."

THE NIGHTCAPS ARE AT A CROSSROADS. Musically, things couldn't be better. They've built up the bank account playing banquets for bigwigs like Nike and Starbucks – and a political fund-raiser whose guests included that oversexed saxman, Bill Clinton – and they've done it doing their own music, not a bunch of cover songs pulled together to appease a workforce. "Though we do know a lot of standards," Dan confesses.

It's "The Nightcaps" that's bugging the Nightcaps. They're worried about their band name, that it might pigeonhole them into a scene – that would be lounge – which has already slipped a bit, in Seattle and other big music markets, thanks to a resurgence of swing. But what's in a name?

"I think in some ways our name has been a thorn in our side," Dan says. "We never would have picked it if we ever thought it would become so associated with a genre. Because we've always been adamant about avoiding the kitsch factor. We didn't want people saying about us, 'Oh, if you've seen 'em once …'"

"Lounge is like any other kind of music," Theresa adds. "It offers differing things within a spectrum. It can be either campy or serious. We're more into the serious side. Our goal is to be entertaining. Not funny, campy and cheesy."

"But sometimes," Dan says, "a song cries out for a gag."

THE CROWD AT THE 700 CLUB has settled into the evening. The band, looking as sharp as it did on *numero uno*, pauses just long enough to allow Theresa to introduce the next song, their snappy cover of Nancy Sinatra's "Last of the Secret Agents." Before launching into it, she dedicates it – in a totally charming manner that disguises her satire – to a sharp-dressed catboy near the front door. When the man recognizes it's *he* whom Theresa has tagged as the honored recipient of this number, he lowers his cropped head, peers out over his … sunglasses!, looks momentarily surprised, then flashes a bewildered grin as his body swaggers and his eyes shift proudly around the room.

I'd never heard the song, and so I'll swear that Theresa Hannam owns it, that it may have been written for Nancy Sinatra but that it belongs to the Nightcaps and their sultry singer.

"He's the last of the secret agents / and he's my man," Hannam belts, with a nod and a wink toward our towering secret agent. Inspired, the big boy shuffles off to the bar for another beer. The Nightcaps play on like there's no tomorrow.

But I know there will be, both for them and for lounge, together or apart. I know that the Nightcaps are going to follow their hunches to where the music takes them. With any luck, that'll be far. And lounge? Well, if it isn't safe in the hands of the Nightcaps, then it's safe somewhere. In another band, in another town and, if in no other place, in my memory.

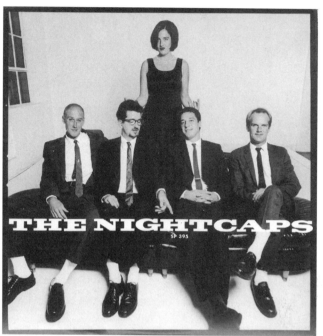

The Nightcaps have a CD, Split, *and two 45s, "I Don't Like You / Love You More" and "Gambler's Game / For Me," on their own label, Rendezvous. Their music is distributed by the Seattle label Sub Pop.*

'Lounge is a live-and-learn kind of thing. You learn that Guy Lombardo sucks, despite the cool cover.' The Nightcaps' Dan Cunneen

Gen Inaba / Matador

Pizzicato Five, modern purveyors of lounge-based rhythms.

Dinner Music for a Pack of Hungry Gen-Xers

[T h e   1 9 9 0 s   L o u n g e   REVIVAL]

By Thomas Conner

A funny thing happened on the road to nowhere.

A sizeable chunk of Generation X decided that we felt neither stupid nor contagious. Kurt Cobain, for all his worthwhile pioneering efforts in rock 'n' roll, just didn't speak for all of us. Nor did the scores of frowning, moping, slovenly kids who came through the doors that Nirvana fell through – all of them baby-faced, inexperienced and begging us to suck their angst. Indeed, some of us felt downright uncomfortable in a culture chafed by denim and overdosing on heroin chic. Really – heroin *chic!*

So while the record industry broke out the lobby soda machines for its younger, disaffected clientele and the flannel-shirt brigades hung shapeless, featureless gypsy rags and coveralls on the unsuspecting youth of America, those of us reared in the neon '80s and freshly set onto career tracks in a revived economy were left to find other soundtracks for our new, upbeat lives. So we did what every generation does when faced with this kind of cultural dichotomy: We looked to the past to usher in an innovative future.

Look at the new fixation on electronic dance music. Synthesized sounds have been heralded as the wave of the future at least twice before, from the pioneering experiments of Kraftwerk and Brian Eno in the early '70s to the computer-savvy sounds of synth bands like Flock of Seagulls and Depeche Mode in the '80s. In the '90s, though, the bite of new electronic sounds sank deeper and spawned a beast with many heads – trip-hop, ambient, acid house, electronica, techno. The new sounds were rhythmically innovative, culturally transcendent and just crisp enough to appeal to those of us on the optimistic and slightly hedonistic side of Generation X. It beat the hell out of recycled power chords and flailing, greasy hair. The culture around electronica – an umbrella term for the genre – encouraged dancing, etiquette, fashion, a bit of romance and an emphasis on experience, which, for good or ill, naturally couples with the pursuit of chemically altered states. The music, you see, was more about the listener's experience than the player's.

Sounds like the parameters of lounge music to me. That music was rhythmically innovative, culturally transcendent and perfectly crisp for the post-war isms, from hedonism to optimism. The goals of lounge musicians in the '50s and '60s were the same as modern-day electronica pioneers – the dancing, ettiquette, fashion, romance and experience. The experience – transporting suburbanites to exotic places around the globe or off-world – back then used intruments and sounds not native to our happy but hum-drum American routines. Taking advantage of the newly available stereo effects helped conjure that altered state, not to mention the music's defining musical aid: the cocktail. The drugs are stronger today, but the music scoring the new experience is directly related to the once-derided schmaltz of old. It's also because of DJs like Dmitri From Paris and bands like Stereolab and Portishead – bookish geeks who researched the beginnings of exotica before making their own electronica – that the 1990s lounge music revival took off like a *Yellow Bird*.

That's just one explanation of lounge music's triumphant return in the century's final decade. There are numerous reasons why the wined and refined sounds of easy listening have struck a chord in a new generation of swingers, and we'll look at those connections here – how the many factors combined to finally give forgotten artists and compsers like Juan Garcia Esquivel and Jean-Jacques Perrey their due. It's easy to over-intellectualize this anti-intellectual movement, so pour a drink and we'll pore through the story of lounge music's unprophesied resurrection in the right frame of mind.

Personally, I think it started with the B-52s. One song in particular, too: "Planet Claire," on the band's eponymous debut. We kids would drop the needle onto this record and wait for the build-up – you know that delicious anticipation. Out of the crackling silence comes a faint beeping, a pulsing communication from space. Suddenly it turn rhythmic, supporting a small-but-mighty battery of toms that have entered the mix, suggesting that this beep-

ing might be transmitting from a jungle out there in space. In comes an electronic, sci-fi flick melody that could have easily been produced on a theremin, and the band's chic alien singer Fred Schneider begins sing-speaking about the mysterious origins of the girl in question, a woman so bizarre she comes from her own planet, a wacky place straight out of the cardboard-saucer black-and-white films. The guitarist props up the whole song with an instantly recognizable riff – copped from Mancini's "Peter Gunn."

When this song trickled out of Athens, Georgia in 1979, Mancini was far from kitsch status and the country's lounge scene was a pit of sexual irresponsibility and low class. The B-52s, though, began boldly presenting their zany art-rock agenda. Theirs was a musical barrage armed with the trappings of the lounge and exotica era – not only the multicolored beehive hairdos of singers Cindy Wilson and Kate Pierson (or Schneider's occasional fez) but the group's taste for old musical sounds that still sounded like transmissions from future Mars colonies and their determination to look absolutely smashing in every circumstance.

The group returned from a brief hiatus in 1998 sounding fresher than ever. They remain the ultimate party band, and their return had more to do with mere '80s nostalgia. The lounge revival had exploded a few years earlier, and though the lounge craze hasn't conquered the mainstream in its second life – much to the joy of the protective scenesters – it had made enough waves and influenced enough mainstream rock acts to open America's ears to wowee sounds. In fact, with hardcore acts employing theremins and pop acts rediscovering the vibraphone, America in the late '90s may be more receptive to lounge and surf sounds than when the B-52s started in 1979. We're in search of something to play at parties again (because we're having parties again!), and Alice in Chains just kills a room.

The aforementioned legions unimpressed by grunge's distorted revolution are of greater numbers than you might think, and not all of us turned to the retreaded oldies coming out of the new Nashville. Instead, we tuned into the strains that scored our urban existences. By the mid-'90s, the polarity made for a striking subculture, as well as an easy explanation for the revival of the old music and fashions. Dean Miller, a Los Angeles lounge DJ at Mr. Phat's Royal Martini Club in actor Johnny Depp's ultra-hip Viper Room, summed up the lounge revival in *The Lust for Lounge* by Robert A. Lindquist, saying, "I see this as the ultimate backlash against grunge. These people have simply come to the realization that it's a whole lot better dressing up, sipping cocktails and smoking cigars, than not showering, wearing ripped up jeans and not getting their hair cut. This harkens back to a time when things were a whole lot classier. The men are cool and sharp, and the women aren't afraid to dress and act like women."

Indeed, despite what most mope-rock wailers will tell you, the human race – particularly in America – is extroverted at heart. We desire the company of others when celebrating and relieving stress, and we desire the consumption of tasty, often alcoholic, beverages whilst doing so. While in the company of others, we wish to shine, to be noticed, to be adored. Perhaps that's why the parties I attended where the Stone Roses' house-music classic "I Wanna Be Adored" was blasting on the hi-fi were loads more fun than any gatherings where "Smells Like Teen Spirit" provided the soundtrack. The former had people smiling, hoisting colored drinks and dancing because the spirit demanded it; the latter was a collage of furrowed brows, insecure small talk and way too much air guitar.

The family connection between that Manchester house scene and the swinging lounge era probably is made in fewer steps than you might think. The impulses were the same, anyway. It, too, was a pre-emptive reaction against grunge rock. Later, the resistence would polarize the American club scene. If grunge was going to be about dressing down, we were going to dress up. If grunge was going to be about catharsis, we were going to be about control. If grunge was going to frown, we were going to smile. No, more than that – hell, Lesley Gore could smile – we were going to cast devilish glances and possibly even leer, be that on a contemporary dance floor or in a retro-kitsch nightclub.

It's no coincidence that electronica and the revived exotica grew simultaneously. The constant search by DJs for more old records to sample turned the world's decommissioned vinyl records into gold. As new hipsters flipped through the endless bins of mid-century LPs, they couldn't help but raise eyebrows at some of the worn covers. These were young, mostly male hipsters doing the hunting, so the alluring sex kittens sprawled across some jackets caught a few eyes. The now-quaint technological bragging "Stereo Action: The Sound Your Eyes Can Follow," "Spectra-Sonic Sound – The Ultimate in High Fidelity," raised a chuckle in CD-reared fan-boys. Also, bawdy titles like *Nice Girls Don't Stay for Breakfast* (Julie London) or *Seymour Gibbons Plays With Himself* had to cause a few DJs to slap a lounge platter on the turntable, saying, "What in the world is this?"

What they found in their amusement turned out to be kinda cool, it stayed on the turntable and a seemingly fresh, welcome scene was born.

Commercial considerations also helped reignite those tiki torches. First, the industry's elimination of the vinyl LP as a productive recording medium only enhanced its mystique. If mom and dad say you can't have it, you're going to go get it, right? That's the attitude that has kept vinyl thoroughly respectable and available in the punk community, as well as the DJ market swiping up LPs from all genres to use in their mixes. Plus, a lot of aging boomers refused to surrender their turntables and – being traditionally anti-authoritarian – were actually inspired by the decommissioning of vinyl to beef up their collections and start hunting it again. The used record stores were filling with cross-generational enthusiasts, not just nostalgia nerds, and they were rifling through the same bins that held Dean Elliott, Alvino Rey and the Three Suns, all waiting to be rediscovered.

The victory of the compact disc over the vinyl LP worked the other way, too. The record labels realized that fans would want to update their collection to include their favorite titles on the new medium,

CDs (some would argue that the labels engineered the change-over in dominant mediums just to seed reissues). They began scouring their catalogs for worthy old albums to reissue on the crisp, new medium. Easy listening titles – Ray Conniff, Mancini, the 101 Strings – once sold in huge figures, so they were ready candidates for digital rebirth. Also, since the labels were going to the trouble of reissuing old titles for existing fans, it was only cost-effective for them to aim their marketing machines at new audiences. Once they got wind of the exotic breezes wafting through clubland, they quickly repsonded with phenomenal series like Capitol's monolithic *Ultra-Lounge* set, RCA's definitive *Space-Age Pop* trio and Rhino's potent *Cocktail Mix*. The cash, as always, was a catalyst.

Once the bandwagon was rolling, hipsters and hipster wanna-bes began jumping aboard from all sides. The reissues of old lounge standards and albums began pouring forth, whether inspired mostly by the retro fashions or its pockets. Some clubs and even a few radio stations – somehow nowadays the last bastions of change – shoved aside their alt-rock schedulings for lounge parties. New "rock" bands cropped up either completely disposed to the retro music or determined to mix the best of old and new sounds without losing the overriding lounge aesthetic.

In fact, certain circles within the rock idiom wholeheartedly embraced lounge music's spunk, sounds and control, not to mention its simultaneous class and underhanded sexuality. Those rockers who weren't in it solely for the catharsis and extended adolescence began tinkering with stereophonics and instrumentation inspired by the newly unearthed easy listening and exotica records. Here is a quick look at lounge music's occasional brushes with modern-day rock 'n' roll:

The Revivalists

San Francisco's **Action Plus** pulls off the modern-retro balancing act with ease. The group's self-titled and self-released '96 CD blends dangerous, espionage guitars with South American rhythms and Ray Conniff-like wordless cooing. It's a lean lounge machine.

If punk and lounge can live side-by-side, so can ska and lounge. **Joe Altruda**'s outfit usually starts with a ska rhythm, but before you know it the song is a swingin' cha-cha or a bossa nova or a mambo. Noted for his appearance on the *Swingers* soundtrack, Altruda doubles his billing as both the loungey *Joey Altruda and the Cocktail Crew* and the more traditionally ska *Jump With Joey*. Recommended: on Will Records, *Cocktails With Joey* and *Kingston Cocktail*.

The Coctails enjoyed a swingin' ride on the lounge revival wave they helped to launch with their debut record, *Hip Hip Hooray*, in 1990 – a year before grunge was the word. This bunch of Kansas City natives recorded four albums for their Hi-Ball label before relocating to Chicago and Carrot Top Records. Their eponymous CD has sold well, but the lounge-jazz group played its last show on New Year's Eve 1995. Leader Archer Prewitt now records solo and with the subtle rock group The Sea and the Cake.

Dmitri From Paris was a bedroom DJ struggling to reconcile his love for old lounge records and new house music. Thank heavens some clubs started letting him spin; otherwise, we might never have been graced with the genius hybrid of old and new sounds that is his debut, *Sacre Bleu* on Atlantic. Fusing the subtle camp, airy instrumentation and a few samples from lounge's golden era to light club beats and extended mixes, Dmitri brings together the ends of the rainbow. Magnifique!

One '60s album from experimental San Francisco troupe **Fifty-Foot Hose** is worth a listen to new lounge junkies. *Cauldron* – an impossible-to-find LP from 1968 that actually found CD release from Weasel Disc in '95 – melds avant-garde rock with the era's best examples of electronic experimentation, including intriguing handling of stereo separation and an Orbital take on "God Bless the Child." The music aims for bluesy psychedelia but falls short – and into a slightly funky space-age bachelor pad.

Lounge was yanked into the mainstream for an instant when the **Mike Flowers Pops** turned its sly, swank, parodic gaze on the Oasis hit "Wonderwall," turning the Britpop ballad into the kind of bopping lounge music.

Austin Powers would dig, baby. Flowers' full-length disc, *A Groovy Place* on London-PolyGram, is full of such treatments – a Vegas-style Velvet Underground medley and a swingin' reading of Prince's "1999" – making him the Weird Al Yankovic of lounge.

The Friends of Dean Martinez are a loose collective featuring past and current members of Giant Sand and Naked Prey. The group's debut, *The Shadow of Your Smile* (Sub Pop, 1995), and follow-up, *Retrograde* (Sub Pop, 1997), are retro sets of guitar instrumentals with a lounge and surf feel. It's more homage than revivalist, but the pieces are infused with enough wit and irony to evoke the twinkle in a hipster's eye.

If man's future in space sounds like the **Gentle People**, let's blast off, baby! This multinational ambient conglomerate swirls together a stew of influences, from highballs and tiki torches to rocket ships and computer bliss. Wired magazine described them, saying, "It's as if Brigitte Bardot, the Aphex Twin and Jason King have all put on multi-colored fun-furs and jetted on to your patio for a fondue party." A few discs on the Rephlex label: *Emotion Heater, Journey, Soundtracks for Living* and *Mix Gently.*

Oi! What's an ethnic lounge li-zahd going to do? Anything, according to the four wacky Midwesterners who formed the **Kabalas**, the world's only polka-klezmer-cocktail-surf-jazz band. Live shows aren't to be missed, nor the CDs, *Martinis and Bagels* (Dionysus, 1996) and *Eye of Zohar* (Dionysus, 1997), featuring such snappy originals as "The Traci Lords Polka," "Death Takes an Ibuprofen," and the cataclysmic showstopper "Hey! Lordy Mambo."

With a name like the **Lounge Lizards**, it's got

Of all the modern rock innovators that helped legitimize fringe musical forms – like lounge, bossa nova and space-age pop, among many others – **Stereolab** leads the pack. This group significantly expands the Cocteau Twins' start-with-rhythm-add-melody formula. They dabble in all the retro recording technology their name implies without ever getting campy. Side projects include a billing as the Groop for Space-Age Bachelor Pad Music. Early records are the loungiest.

England's Stereolab have long dabbled in synthetics and program loops that invoke an American lounge music ethic. Below, the cover of the band's 1994 release, Mars Audiac Quintet.

*New swing
sensation, the
Cherry Poppin'
Daddies.*

to be good, right? Well, the music's good, but it's not quite what we refer to as "lounge." These prototype hepcats were retro before retro was cool, dressing like swingers and covering "Harlem Nocturne" with a more avant-garde and bop flair. The first, self-titled album (1982) is the best.

Verrill Keene is a Now new find on Del-Fi Records. His light and lovely 1996 debut, *An Afternoon Affair*, features a divine retelling of "Norwegian Wood" alongside several dreamy originals. A Show Town Records ad described him thusly: "The pretty people are Verrill Keene's people. His any-hour music makes everybody feel just a little bit lovelier."

If you've got the lineage, flaunt it. Matt Brubeck – of the Brubecks – leads the zany San Francisco outfit known as the **Oranj Symphonette**. The group's one disc, *The Oranj Symphonette Plays Mancini* (Hi Fi-Gramavision, 1996), mixes up the jazz combo formula with zither, bird calls and slide whistles. It won't be an easy album for Mancini fans to digest; the tribute is respectful but some-

times chaotic. These are, after all, players fresh from sessions with Tom Waits, PJ Harvey and the like.

Japan runneth over with retro acts, as if our kitschy lounge recordings from decades ago have just reached those rocky shores. **Pizzicato Five** led the charge with their warm, revivalist reconstructions of American pop and easy listening. Their sound collages include bits from every genre of music, notably exotica, lounge and spy scores. The duo had numerous albums in Japan before coming stateside on Matador. 1995's *The Sound of Music* is a good start.

And don't forget the swing kids. The revival of hot swing in the '90s has rippled the mainstream more, and many clubs tend to cater to both swing and lounge crowds. Notable new swing bands are **Big Bad Voodoo Daddy** (another bunch of hepcats that owes its life and royalties to the film *Swingers*), Indigo Swing (more modern-day swingers on *All Aboard!*), the **Royal Crown Revue** (the high-step-

In '68, a young David Bowie wrote a lyric for a French chanson called "Comme d'Habitude."

Kevin Davies/BMG

pers playing for Jim Carrey in *The Mask*, with a swingin' debut called Mugzy's Move), the **Cherry Poppin' Daddies** (named for a bit of sexual slang, they started the "Zoot Suit Riot" via Mojo Records in '98) and the **Brian Setzer Orchestra** (former Stray Cats leader started touring with his 16-piece band and monogrammed music stands the year grunge broke; it took a while for us to realize how great his new swing was, and he broke in 1998 when his Louis Prima cover from "The Dirty Boogie" scored a Gap commercial).

The Impressionable

The Cardigans have made some of the most pleasant pop of the '90s, due to their lounge music fascinations and their heavy metal backgrounds. Using old recording and instrument technologies, they scored hits from their slightly retro-sounding pop record Life – full of vibes, music box chimes and a recognizable lounge sensibility, thanks in no small part to the cooing vocals of Nina Persson.

Combustible Edison wound up being the god-fathers of the lounge revival – a delicious irony con-sidering they were signed to Seattle's Sub Pop label, which broke Nirvana's "Nevermind."

This New England-based bunch of neo-swingers grew from the ashes of a modern rock band called Christmas. They mix up crooning ballads and spy music with traditional lounge and exotica. They enjoyed middling success with their CDs *I, Swinger* and *Schizophonic* before providing the fabulous soundtrack to the awful film *Four Rooms*.

When electro-pop practitioners **Devo** ducked into easy listening, it wasn't much of a stretch. The seminal new wave band's 1987 release, *E-Z Listening Disc*, finds them retooling 19 of their own tracks – including "Girl U Want" and "Whip It" – for the electro-schmaltzy instrumental ouevre. It's meant to be amusing, but it often misses that mark.

Talk about switching gears. Legendary punk guitarist East Bay Ray emerged from the ashes of the Dead Kennedys to turn about and launch **Frenchy**, a swinging lounge band. Lead singer Carla followed a similarly surprising connection: She was inspired to lounge music after watching the Circle Jerks' appearance as a lounge act in the cult film *Repo Man*. Together, the two created a band in which they could still play Black Flag songs – only now they play the scorching solos on marimbas. Two discs on Dionysus, *Bumps and Grinds* and *Che's Lounge*.

Love Jones would be one schmaltzy rock band if the lounge revival hadn't been around to help define them. This bleary Hollywood-by-way-of-Louisville collective was formed by two former rockers (like ex-Lemonheads drummer Ben Daughtrey) and now plays everything from bossa nova to crooning and doo-wop. Two releases on Zoo, 1994's *Here's to the Losers* and 1995's *Powerful Pain Relief*.

After the dissolution of San Francisco's legendary power pop band Jellyfish, Roger Manning went onto his deeper retro pursuits in a duo called the **Moog Cookbook**. On two releases – self-titled and *Ye Olde Space Band Plays Classic Rock Hits*, both on Restless – and in some dynamic, space-suited live shows, the pair retool old pop and rock standards on Moogs to alternately trying and hilarious effect.

David Johansen really just went from one glam outfit to another. Long after his seminal flashy punk band the New York Dolls dissolved, Johansen began appearing in nightclubs as a semi-comic, semi-spicy lounge act called Buster Poindexter. The gigs landed him another contract, which produced a few albums and a hit with the soca favorite "Hot Hot Hot."

Van Halen lost its spark when **David Lee Roth** left – because how do you replace a showman like this? Before completely sliding into self-parody, Roth's first solo effort – an EP called *Crazy From the Heat* (Warner Bros., 1985) – features several choice and chunky lounge moments, from his hit tribute to Louis Prima in "Just a Gigolo/I Ain't Got Nobody" to the high kicks of "Coconut Grove."

Lounge lizards down South aren't afraid of the low-brow connotations in listening to **Southern**

Culture on the Skids. The leering trio plays rocka-hillbilly with a delightful wit and often delves into lounge territory, from breezy tracks like "Make Mayan a Hawaiian" from *Dirt Track Date* (Geffen, 1996) to their 1997 remake of "House of Bamboo."

Lounge aficionados gave each other looks when **Us3**'s "Cantaloop (Flip Fantasia)" became a pop hit in 1994. The jazzy rap single sampled Herbie Hancock's "Cantaloupe Island," which Pucho and the Latin Soul Brothers made into a fluid lounge hit in the '60s.

THE DABBLERS

David Bowie joined Bing Crosby for a 1977 television-special duet of "Little Drummer Boy."

That single has been overlicensed to numerous Christmas compilations. His other connection to lounge music is a lesser-known but infinitely more fascinating tale, recently told in Q magazine. In '68, a young Bowie wrote a lyric for a French chanson called "Comme d'Habitude." Bowie's song, "Even a Fool Learns to Love," was packed with dreamy images of lonely parties and melancholy clowns, but no one picked it up. Instead, the same French tune was used for some lyrics by Paul Anka, who pitched the song to Sinatra – "My Way."

According to Q, "Bowie sulked for some years, writing 'Life on Mars' as a mocking pastiche." A similarly styled French tune-to-Bowie's words song, "Pancho," turns up on a recent compilation from RCA, *Another Crazy Cocktail Party!*

You might not expect ex-banker **Harry Nilsson** – singer-songwriter, rock-era hitmaker ("Without You") and John Lennon drinkin' bud – to show up in a lounge-music book, but *A Little Touch of Schmilsson in the Night* (RCA APL1-0097, 1973) fits the bill, and more. It's a collection of standards, from "Makin' Whoopee" to the *Casablanca* classic, "As Time Goes By," each one taken at a pace that would have to speed up to crawl, with Harry delivering the words as though he had the weight of the world, or at least a brace of martinis, on his shoulders. Sinatra cohort Gordon Jenkins arranged and conducted.

Robert Palmer – that stoney-faced, sharply dressed bloke who enjoys an unusual rock career mostly of covers – adds a surprisingly snazzy reading of "(Love Is) The Tender Trap" to the overlooked soundtrack to *True Romance*, a Tony Scott film scripted by Quentin Tarrantino (who's own musical tastes and resulting soundtracks did a lot to turn more heads toward the gone-but-not-forgotten). Palmer had tried standards before on his 1992 outing, *Ridin' High*, almost a simply irresistable collection of adult music, like a sprightly take on "Witchcraft" and the big-band brass of "Hard Head."

She deserves the blame for bringing the Eagles together, but at least she tried to spread her wings later in her career. **Linda Ronstadt** eschewed her country-rock roots in the '80s to tackle several sets of standards with Nelson Riddle and his orchestra. Each of these albums – *What's New*, *Lush Life* and *For Sentimental Reasons* – is tame, tepid and not exactly suited to Ronstadt's leathery pipes, but they were commercially successful and brought a touch of elegance to mid-'80s pop radio, which really, really needed it.

Occasional genius **Todd Rundgren** tried to capitalize on the lounge revival in 1997 on *With a Twist*, an album of his own previously recorded songs retooled as acoustic lounge numbers. Knowing Rundgren's production flair, it sounds like a promising and fun project, but "Hello, It's Me" and "It Wouldn't Have Made Any Difference" simply don't translate from FM to orthophonic high fidelity. Would have been a great EP, but the well-meaning humor fizzles midway through this full-length disc.

THE COLLECTIONS

For a taste of spy music, check out *Secret Agent S.O.U.N.D.S.* (Mai Tai, 1995), featuring Combustible Edison and numerous other revival-

era acts. Not far off that disc's dangerous mission is *Shots in the Dark* (Donna-Del-Fi, 1996), a Mancini tribute with his spy music and lush lounge interpretted by the Cramps' Poison Ivy, the Oranj Symphonette, Friends of Dean Martinez, Brother Cleve and His Lush Orchestra and many more.

A decent round-up of rockish lounge lizards is *Livin' Lounge: The Fabulous Sounds of Now!* (Continuum, 1995), including Love Jones, Buster Poindexter, the Wonderful World of Joey and more.

For the more rakish and restless of lounge tastes, sip from *Cocktail Companion* (Estrus), a compilation focusing on wilder, hillbilly acts like Southern Culture on the Skids and neo-surf bands like Man or Astroman?

Lounge-a-Palooza (Hollywood, 1997) was a hit-or-miss effort, but when it hits – ooh, baby. It's an unfocused lounge tribute with chaff like Poe and Fun Lovin' Criminals, but occasional insight from Edwyn Collins ("Witchcraft") and the James Taylor Quartet ("Music to Watch Girls By"). The one-two punch, though, is a supergroup – Glen Campbell, Michelle Shocked, Freddy Fender, Sheila E. and the Texas Tornados – doing "Wichita Lineman" and a truly exquisite arrangement of Soundgarden's "Black Hole Sun" sung by Steve Lawrence and Eydie Gorme.

last call

Had enough yet? If not, read on for a selection of clubs, record shops and other places that purvey lounge music and information on lounge music for the serious connoisseur.

Kelly Kurt

shops

ALL MUSIC SERVICES
530 14th St. #9
San Francisco, CA 94103
phone (415) 864-8222
fax (415) 864-7222
allmusic@wco.com
A mail-order and search service specializing in exotica and lounge vinyl. Helpful and thorough.

ALL SALES ARE VINYL
brunner@asavinyl.com
http://www.asavinyl.com/
This Los Angeles-area storehouse runs the gamut from Belafonte to the Beastie Boys. Stock includes many lounge titles. The name indicates the format available. Since 1987, the store has organized the Greater Orange County Monthly Record Shows, usually featuring 100+ dealers and special guests (they once had Yma Sumac) at the Sequoia Club, 7530 Orangethorpe Avenue, Buena Park, Calif. Catalog available online.

ALL VINYL RECORDS
1695 Rambling Woods Drive
Lawrenceville, GA 30043
phone/fax: (770) 822-1772
tonylenz@avana.net
LPs, 45s, 78s in broad range of categories. Catalog available for downloading at http://www.all-vinyl.com/.

AMOEBA MUSIC
2455 Telegraph Avenue
Berkeley, CA
(510) 549-1125
1855 Haight Street
San Francisco, CA
(415) 831-1200
http://www.amoebamusic.com/
The San Francisco store of this vinyl-tape-CD dealer is worth a stop. Decent pickings for lounge platters. No catalogs or ordering available online.

ARCHAIC IDIOT
1720 N. Vermont
Los Angeles, CA 90027
(213) 953-8896
The ads encourage us to "visit the best tourist trap in town," but the bins are full of serious thrills for collectors, particularly of lounge and exotica, as well as the extremely exotic and bizarre.

BEDAZZLED DISCS
911 E. Pine St.
Seattle, WA 98122
phone (206) 329-6500
fax (206) 329-6111
bdazzled@cnw.com
http://www.cnw.com/~bdazzled/
New and used vinyl. Complete listings online, including categories for Easy and Brazilian.

CALIFORNIA ALBUMS
P.O. Box 3426
Hollywood, CA 90078-3426
fax (213) 461-4862
calalbums@earthlink.net
http://www.californiaalbums.com/
Online and mail-order vinyl auction. LPs, plus a few CDs. More than 60 categories, including numerous lounge-inclusive ones and a vast instrumental selection. Watch for their extensive, notoriously small-print ads, but only if a magnifying glass is handy.

CYRCO MUSIC
(COLLECTORS OF YESTERDAY'S RECORDINGS COMPANY)
3811 Leavenworth St.
Omaha, NE 68105
phone (402) 345-8164
fax (402) 346-2755
jeffcyr@cyrcomusic.com
http://www.cyrcomusic.com/
A private vinyl LP dealer with more than 70,000 titles, including an impressive Easy Listening sec-

tion with a penchant for the pop vocalists. Catalog available for search online.

FOOTLIGHTS RECORDS
113 East 12th St.
New York, NY 10003
(212) 533-1572
Modest store with a healthy selection of lounge titles.

GOLDEN OLDIES RECORDS
201 N.E. 45th St.
Seattle, WA 98105
phone (206) 547-2260
fax (425) 747-4566
oldies@ix.netcom.com
http://www.goldenoldies-records.com/
Warehouse of hard-to-find vinyl records, reaching back to the 1920s. Excellent free want list service. CD catalog online.

HIGHLAND RECORDS
1617 Bardstown Rd.
Louisville, KY
(502) 451-8805
md@highlandrecords.com
http://www.win.net/md/
Vinyl dealer with decent Easy Listening section. Catalog available online soon.

HITSVILLE RECORD MART
217 King St.
Alexandria, VA 22314
(703) 683 4583
notrico@ix.netcom.com
Good selection of lounge and exotica vinyl, plus some other oddities.

INTOXICA!
231 Portobello Road
London W11 1LT
U.K.
phone 44 (0)171 229 8010
fax 44 (0)171 792 9778
intoxica@intoxica.demon.co.uk
http://www.demon.co.uk/intoxica/
London vinyl-only dealer with listings for Easy, Exotica (with subsection for Moog, old and new), Latin, Bachelor Pad and Sleazy Listening. Lists available online.

JACK DIAMOND MUSIC
450 Oak Grove Ave. #104
Menlo Park, CA 94025
(415) 325-2284
Dyemund@best.com
Bay Area radio personality Jack Diamond also shares his extensive record collection with buyers.

KEN STONE RECORDS
5837 Karric Square Dr. #296
Dublin, OH 43016
phone (614) 766-7844
fax (614) 792-8289
kstone6@juno.com
http://www.csmonline.com/stone/
Modest but intriguing stock of vinyl, featuring three different Easy Listening categories and three separate Sinatra classifications. Catalog available for search online.

M & L RECORDS
6504 Ravenna Ave. N.E.
Seattle, WA 98115
phone (206) 522-8189
mlrecmod@halcyon.com
http://www.halcyon.com/mlrecmod/
Vinyl dealer. Impressive offering in the Pop Instrumental category. Catalog available online.

MUSIC BY MAIL
P.O. Box 368
Palm City, FL 34991

phone (800) 233-3000
phone (407) 286-8502
fax (407) 286-4543
emusic@gate.net
http://www.musicbyemail.com/

This CD-only dealer specializes in discs from Europe and Japan – where so many great lounge reissues have surfaced. The impressive selection definitely runs along the lounge lines, too. Lists and ordering available online.

PAULA'S HOUSE OF MUSIC
8205 Geneva Ave.
Lubbock, TX 79423-2823
phone (806) 793-0111
fax (806) 793-0111
paula@houseofmusic.com
http://houseofmusic.com/

Vinyl dealer . Great listings under an Exotica/SABPM/Easy category. Catalog and ordering available online.

PONK RECORDS
P.O. Box 3664
Bloomington, IL 61702
phone (309) 365-4491
fax (309) 365-1900

A vinyl enclave that welcomes revivalist hipsters, billing itself as "the alternative to alternative music."

PRIMO EARGASMS
2011 King St.
Honolulu, HI 96817
(808) 955-7731

Vinyl and CD dealer specializing in Asian and original pressings from the lounge era. Many wild and wonderful Polynesian delights. Mail-order catalog available.

RECORD FINDERS
P.O. Box 1047
Glen Allen, VA 23060
phone (804) 266-1154
fax (804) 264-9660

MEMORY LANE RECORDS (THE RETAIL OUTLET)
8409 Glazebrook
Richmond, VA 23228
(804) 264-0300
http://www.recordfinders.com/

Vinyl dealer with huge stock and extensive newsletter. Look at the Set Price Items for a gold-mine of lounge platters. Catalog, ordering and some Real Audio samples available online.

RECORD OUTLET
1489 E. Thousand Oaks Blvd., Suite A1
Thousand Oaks, CA 91360
(805) 371-0574
kcrecords@aol.com

A vinyl dealer dedicated to the format. In addition to the medium-sized selection – including some lounge here and there – this store carries turntable supplies and repairs them. Every third Sunday they host a record and collectibles swap meet.

RECORD SURPLUS
11609 W. Pico Blvd.
West Los Angeles, CA
(310) 478-4217

Billing itself as "the last record store," Record Surplus is worth the stop if you have time to comb. Lounge selections don't exactly shine, but the Attic – where no LP or 45 is more than 92 cents – is worth burrowing through. No mail order.

ROCKAWAY RECORDS
2395 Glendale Blvd
Los Angeles, CA 90039
(213) 664-3232 ext. 2
sales@rockaway.com
http://www.rockaway.com/

International vinyl and CD dealer with stores also in Arizona and Australia. Occasional 99-cent sales and parking lot sales are worth thumbing through. Catalog and ordering available online.

RECORD RON'S
239 Chartres St.
New Orleans, LA 70130

phone (504) 522-2239

fax (504) 527-0934

mail order (800) 234-6889

e-mail: recordron@recordron.com

http://recordron.com/

Just two blocks off Canal Street, Record Ron's is a necessary diversion from the many diversions of the Crescent City. Walls and boxes of vinyl are bound to turn up treasures. Staff is friendly and helpful, too. As the ads say, "Tell me I sent you."

SATURN RECORDS

5488 College Ave.

Oakland, CA 94618

phone (510) 654-0335

fax (510) 654-4386

info@saturnrecords.com

http://www.saturnrecords.com/

Beautiful graphics on this vinyl and CD dealer's web site, plus an extensive and knowledgable Easy Listening section broken down into succinct classifications. Lists and ordering available online. Also features newsletter, the Intimate Mood Quarterly.

SONIC RECOLLECTIONS

2701 S.E. Belmont St.

Portland, OR 97214

phone (503) 236-3050

fax (503) 235-1645

orderdesk@sonicrec.com

http://www.sonicrec.com/

Vinyl dealer with a weird and wacky bent. Easy Listening titles are impressive. Catalog and ordering available online.

TIME WARP RECORDS

P.O. Box 5296

Petaluma, CA 94955-5296

fax (707) 766-9757

http://www.vintage.com/record/

Mail-order vinyl dealer with broad scope but intriguing categories. In addition to the lounge titles under Mood-Exotic-Strange Music, look into other technical categories such as Mobile Fidelity Sound Labs for unusual pressings. Catalog available online.

WEIRD HAROLD'S

411 Jefferson Street

P.O. Box 981

Burlington, IA 52601

phone (800) 448-8120

phone (319) 753-5353

e-mail: weirdhar@interl.net

http://www.weirdharolds.com/weird.cgi

Vinyl dealer. Thorough list of available lounge titles. Catalog and ordering available online.

WORLD WIDE WAX

phone (602) 581-5966

fax (602) 530-2950

tim@worldwidewax.com

http://www.worldwidewax.com/

Impressive online catalogs of vintage vinyl, plus scores of scanned album covers. Occasional exotica, lounge and other auctions are not to be missed. Ordering and bidding available online.

clubs

Arizona

COPPER QUEEN COCKTAIL LOUNGE
6933 N. Seventh St.
Phoenix
(602) 274-2650
An airy cocktail bar that's home to the Swank d'Amour party every Valentine's Day and sometimes two or three other times a year. It's a great party, designed to accentuate the mingling as much as the music.

California

J.P.'S RESTAURANT AND LOUNGE
1333 Hollywood Way
Burbank
(818) 845-1800
Offers jazz, pop and lounge music beginning at 9 p.m. Live music ranges from light blues to piano-bar tinkling, with a variety show each Friday night. No cover.

THE DRESDEN ROOM RESTAURANT
1760 N. Vermont Ave.
Los Angeles
(213) 665-4294
A real lounge-era restaurant where you and your date can eat prime rib, drink unique cocktails (order their notorious Blood and Sand) and hear music meant for the dining experience.

THE ENCOUNTER
at Los Angeles International Airport
Noted L.A. lounge DJs Senor Amor and Joey Seehee have given new meaning to "Come Fly With Me" by trying valiantly to create a scene at this airport lounge. It's a great scene with the airport's aura that's worth the trek. Amor spins Friday nights and both host live music on Saturdays.

THE HOLLYWOOD ROOSEVELT HOTEL
7000 Hollywood Blvd
Los Angeles
(213) 466-7000
A luscious old Hollywood hang-out featuring live music and a lobby made for lounging. Errol Flynn allegedly invented his own gin cocktail behind the barber shop.

THREE OF CLUBS
Santa Monica and Vine
Los Angeles
Senor Amor from KXLU's "Molotov Cocktail Hour" spins lounge music live on Wednesday nights.

KOMA COCKTAIL LOUNGE
333 East 1st St.
Los Angeles (Little Tokyo)
(213) 625-9111
Great dive bar with thick Oriental theme. No cover. No drink minimum.

MR. PHAT'S ROYAL MARTINI CLUB
8852 W Sunset Blvd
West Hollywood
(310) 358-1880
Part of Johnny Depp's Viper Room, this is the Gen-X capital of swank. High dress is welcome, if not expected. DJ Dean Miller spins lounge music old and new, and the cocktails are impressive.

RITZ-CARLTON HUNTINGTON HOTEL
1401 S Oak Knoll Ave, Pasadena, CA 91106-4508
(626) 568-3900
Pasadena
Martini hours every day in this crusty old lounge. Order a traditional "cigar dinner" in the restaurant. Light jazz piano playing pretty much constantly.

THE RED FOX INN
2223 El Cajon Blvd.

San Diego
(619) 297-1313

Nice lounge featuring Miss Shirley Ellen with a combo each weekend.

BACKFLIP

601 Eddy St.
San Francisco
(415) 771-FLIP

Majestic fountains adorn this ocean-themed lounge with a great round bar. Includes a seating area with shag carpeting and a few, er, private cabanas.

BRUNO'S

2389 Mission St.
San Francisco
phone (415) 550-7455
fax (415) 642-9059

All the trappings: the red booths, the swell bar, the expensive valet parking. This noted lounge hosts many of the city's newest lounge acts and on Sundays features a Hawaiian band with an 82-year-old slack-key player.

CAFE MARS

798 Brannan St.
San Francisco
phone (415) 621-6277
fax (415) 621-6404

The Martian theme is a bit overworked here, but the scene is vibrant and the cocktails inventive. Don't mind the beers on tap.

THE CHAMELEON CLUB

924 Valencia St. #136
San Francisco
(415) 821-1891

Publishers of the Tiki News throw a Tiki Party at this Mission district lounge once a month. Call for details or visit Tiki's web site at http://www.indieweb.com/tiki/.

THE HI-BALL LOUNGE

473 Broadway
San Francisco
(415) 397-9464

The Bay Guardian described the decor as "the Flintsones meet El Morocco," referring to the paper palms, the tiger-print wall, the red benches. Once known as the Jazz Workshop (with regulars like Theolonious Monk and Charlie Parker), the Hi-Ball Lounge caters to lounge and swing crowds, with swank atmosphere and a large dancefloor.

LILO LOUNGE

1469 18th St.
San Francisco
(415) 643-5678

Great views of downtown San Fran from this Tiki-themed lounge on Potrero Hill. Lounge music. Asian food served daily and a happy hour from 5 to 7 p.m.

RADIO VALENCIA

1199 Valencia St.
San Francisco
(415) 826-1199

A swingin' show every Saturday with the Tiki News' Otto von Stroheim and DJ The Now Sounds throwing down classic lounge and soundtracks. Real pros at handling the scene in this comfy club.

RED ROOM

827 Sutter St.
San Francisco
(415) 346-7666

A slick, urban lounge that lives up to its name – you'll see red everywhere you turn.

THE WEREPAD

2430 Third St.
San Francisco
hotline (415) 824-7334
Doors open at 9:30 p.m. for lounging

Screenings at 10:30 p.m.

http://www.werepad.com/

This theater is a wacky hangout for wacky folks. Movies are "underground revival cinema," which can stretch from 1957 teen poregnancy chronicle "Eighteen and Anxious" to "Hells Angels '69," a loving account of the motorcycle gang in Las Vegas. A hipster hangout before and after the shows.

STARDUST LOUNGE

299 Ninth St.

San Francisco

(415) 861-2983

This lounge goes for the Vegas aesthetic and has been host to parties for Scamp Records and the Tiki News.

BIMBO'S 365

1025 Columbus

San Francisco

(415) 474-0365

A large and bustling place – too bustling most of the time. Crowds, not all of them lounge, shove their way by the cigarette girls and usually miss the point of the ambiance. Korla Pandit played here recently.

CAFE DUNORD

2170 Market, in the Castro

San Francisco

(415) 861-5016

An intriguing lounge in a former speakeasy. Mondays feature Sense-O-Round with exotica and lounge music. Wednesday nights feature the Down Hear Experimental Lounge with live lounge music in styles old and new. The crowd likes to dress up and be groovy.

THE USUAL

400 S. First St.

San Jose

(408) 298-9375

Check out the Limbo Lounge for an eclectic mix of oldies with serious nods toward lounge. Live swing bands on Sundays.

MONSOON CAFE

1212 Third St. Promenade

Santa Monica

(310) 576-9996

The rattan bar in the restaurant downstiars is worth some time, but the music lounge upstairs is where it's happening. Live music ranges from loungey vocalists to Brazilian bands. No cover.

Illinois

THE FANMARKER CLUB

221 W. Frost St.

Rantoul

(217) 893-CLUB

Fine restaurant and club with a separate hardwood-floor ballroom. The lounge has a dynamite jukebox and occasionally features DJs. The restaurant is open until 9 p.m.

Massachusetts

THE BAY TOWER

60 State St.

Boston

(617) 723-1666

Lovely lounge with a breathtaking view of Boston Harbor. Lounge piano during the week and live bands on weekends.

BILL'S BAR AND LOUNGE

9 Lansdowne St.

Boston

(617) 421-9678

Normally a rock-oriented club of little interest to lounge lizards, until Combustible Edison's Brother Cleve hosts "Swank" each Wednesday night, spinning his usual web of swingin' intrigue. Minimal cover.

THE UPSTAIRS LOUNGE

65 Causeway St.

Boston

(617) 299-6951

http://www.cybercom.net/~forrest/sugarbabys.htm

Light swing and heavy lounge here each Thursday with Big Daddy. Sundays are a special lounge blowout, too.

LIZARD LOUNGE
1667 Massachusetts Ave
Cambridge
(617) 547-0759
Underneath the Cambridge Common restaurant, this intimate lounge is loaded with plush Oriental carpets and lush American cocktails. Diverse music with some outrageous live acts on weekends. Cover varies.

REGATTABAR
1 Bennett St
Cambridge
(617) 661-5000
Mellow, upscale jazz bar in the Charles Hotel with great cocktails and service. Music ranges from light jazz to worldly lounge. Expensive cover.

SATURNALIA!
1667 Mass Avenue
Cambridge
(617) 547-0759
Fine lounge scene with a modern edge. DJ Brother Cleve (Combustible Edison keyboardist extraordinaire) often spins here.

CLUB BOHEMIA
425 Washington St.
Somerville
(617) 491-9640
Nondescript lounge in the Kirkland Cafe featuring live music acts with names like Mickey Bliss Organ Combo, the Ken Clark Organ Trio and Wheelers and Dealers.

Michigan

THE VELVET LOUNGE
29 S. Saginaw St.
Pontiac
(248) 334-7411

On this town's newly revived strip, this narrow club caters to dancers and slouchers alike, with both a smattering of pool tables and a built-in cigar humidor. High dress won't be out of sorts here. Music leans toward swing, though on Saturdays things run a bit farther south of the border.

Minnesota

THE FRONT
15 Fourth St. NE
Minneapolis
(612) 378-5115
The Twin Cities' ultimate lounge, in the Ground Zero Niteclub. Catch Vic Volare and the Volare Lounge Orchestra every Tuesday and Bondage A Go-Go every Thursday, but don't miss out on Club Velvet, a great lounge party each Saturday hosted by King Kini.

THE WABASHA STREET CAVES
215 Wabasha St. South
St. Paul
(612) 224-1191
Just what the name says: actual caves once used as a gangster hideout and a speakeasy. A unique and classy club for lounge lizards of all stripes, with lively music and dancing. Swing music every Thursday.

New York

THE BLUE LOUNGE
625 Broadway
New York City (Manhattan)
(212) 473-8787
The hottest Latin music in New York, decorated with Mexican art and featuring a bar the length of a city block – the longest in town. Live music from mambo to salsa.

CANDY BAR AND GRILL
131 Eighth Ave.
New York City (Manhattan)
(212) 229-9702
A bracing little lounge with padded vinyl walls –

yellow, not red – and funky wall lamps. Lovely bartenders and great cocktails. Thursdays are Lounge Nights with DJ Pez spinning lounge sounds.

DEN OF THIEVES
145 E. Houston St.
New York City (Manhattan)
(212) 477-5005
Lounge and some swing bands every Thursday. Smart bartending.

DON HILL'S
511 Greenwich Street
New York City (Manhattan)
(212) 219-2850
About every month, the club hosts a Retro Music Extravaganza, featuring live lounge, swing and rockabilly bands.

GLOBAL 33
93 2nd Ave
New York City (Manhattan)
(212) 477-8427
A totally unique club, designed allegedly as an homage to 1960s Danish airports. Hmm. Live lounge DJs almost nightly.

PAGEANT BAR AND GRILL
109 East 9th St.
New York City (Manhattan)
(212) 529-5333
The Stork Club is a Wednesday night party here hosted by DJ Swanky Don. He mixes up the standard exotica and dance music of lounge with a lot of classic crooners from Dino to Sinatra. Cool room and wise bartenders. No cover.

TEDDY'S
96 Berry St.
New York City (Brooklyn)
(718) 384-9787
Cozy neighborhood lounge features a lounge DJ on Tuesdays. Eye candy includes a live go-go dancer on a pedastal. No cover.

WINDOWS ON THE WORLD
One World Trade Center, 107th Floor
New York City (Manhattan)
(212) 524-7000
This posh lounge offers a striking aerial view of Manhattan. DJ Lucien serves up worldly lounge sounds on Wednesdays for his Mondo 107 party, peppered with a little light techno. No cover. Some live swing bands on weekends for a $10 cover. Tuesdays is another loungey theme called "Koombah Woombah."

North Carolina

TRESSAS DOWNTOWN JAZZ AND BLUES
28 Broadway
Asheville
(704) 254-7072
Described by some dance afficiandos as Asheville's "center of the local Martini Nation colony."

Ohio

THE SPY CLUB
1261 W. Sixth St.
Cleveland
(216) 621-7907
An swank club in the city's warehouse district becomes Mr. Slick's Jive Shack on Thursday nights. The club DJ mixes up big band and lounge sounds, and about every other week they have live music.

CITI LOUNGE
114 Louisiana Ave.
Perrysburg
(419) 872-6437
Swing bands in this near-Toledo club every weekend, but this crowd isn't here to dance. Cocktails and clothes are the order of the evening.

Oklahoma

THE RED ROOM
18 E. Brady St.
Tulsa
(918) 582-2439

A tiny lounge next to (and owned by) the Hercules Motor Co. dance club, the Red Room is an undiscovered cocktail lounge. Bartenders are usually stumped by orders for drinks they didn't chug at their college frat houses, but the place is cozy.

Pennsylvania

THE FIVE SPOT
1 S. Bank St.
Philadelphia
(215) 574-0070
A sly little supper club with a great lounge. Weekly poker night.

Texas

THE RED JACKET
3606 Lower Greenville Ave.
Dallas
(214) 823-4747
Thursdays are Martini Jazz nights at this mellow club with a sunken dance floor. Free dance lessons at 8 p.m. for the swing crowd.

THE FABULOUS SATELLITE LOUNGE
3616 Washington Ave.
Houston
(713) 869-COOL
http://www.fabsat.com/
The live music is a popular lure here, but the small touches make the scene. Monday nights feature cheap drink specials and, yes, bingo.

ORCHID LOUNGE
2415 Dunstan
Houston
(713) 524-0228
Don't miss Lucky LaRue's Swinging Cocktail Party most Tuesday nights. Weekends feature live music from touring lounge and swing bands. Lively atmosphere and a little something for everyone.

UROPA
3302 Mercer
Houston
(713) 627-1132
Duck into the Frank lounge here for tiki torches and fancy fabrics. Great atmosphere.

Vancouver, B.C.

THE WALDORF HOTEL
507-318 Homer St.
Vancouver
(604) 253-7141
The inimitable Waldorf is home to a handful of timeless Polynesian lounges – the Polynesian Room, the Tahitian Twilight Lounge and the Menehune Hut – that opened originally in 1955 and were shut down for a time over objections to the black-velvet paintings of naked Tahitian women on the walls. Each Saturday is the grand Blue Lizard Cocktail Club and Supper Soiree, when the lounges are filled with hundreds of blue candles and swingers of every ilk. For information on this party, call (604) 685-1133 or dial up http:www.webpool.com/bluelizard.

NIAGRA HOTEL PUB
435 W. Pender
Vancouver
(604) 688-7574
Cozy lounge featuring live bands of all sorts, but Wednesdays are reserved for the lush life with the Gin and Sin Lounge party. Dress well.

Washington

THE CLOUD ROOM
1619 9th Ave.
Seattle
(206) 292-6206
Great piano lounge with an aerial view of the city from the 11th floor of the downtown Camlin Hotel. Relaxed atmosphere, good bar and delightful piano jazz.

DYNAMITE LOUNGE
15 Lake St. S.
Kirkland

(425) 822-3474

The Jet City Swingers mix up lounge and swing on the first and third Wednesdays of each month.

PAMPAS CLUB
90 Wall St.
Seattle
(206) 728-1140

Crisp club with good drinks. Music on weekends is mostly light dance tunes from the '40s through the '60s.

Washington, D.C.

THE BACKDOOR LOUNGE
3rd Street at Pioneer Square
Washington, D.C.
(202) 546-5979

Atmosphereic little place with a lounge DJ on Fridays and live music on Saturdays. Dress code. Cover $4.

publications

TIKI NEWS
2215-R Market St. #177
San Francisco, CA 94114
ottotemp@aol.com
http://www.indieweb.com/tiki/

Lounge music's pace car on the information highway, the bimonthly Tiki News has done more than most to spread the word about lounge. Editor Otto von Stroheim is particularly interested (obviously) in the exotic side of things – claiming, "It is our mission to preserve any and all remaining elements from the Polynesian Pop era of the mid 1950s to mid 1970s" – but all lounge music has benefitted from his journalistic class act.

COOL AND STRANGE MUSIC! MAGAZINE
P.O. Box 8501
Everett, WA 98201
fax (206) 303-3404
coolstrge@aol.com
members.aol.com/coolstrge/coolpage.html
editor Dana Countryman

A great quarterly 'zine focused on the wilder side of recorded music, with a definite emphasis on lounge and its more zany practitioners. Frequent interviews and features about noted lounge stars, plus reviews. Always educational.

EXOTICA/ET CETERA
1401 Ravenhurst Dr.
Raleigh, NC 27615
phone (919) 846-9571
fax (919) 846-9507
vinyllives@earthlink.net

Informational occasional 'zine and catalog organized by R. Preston Peek "celebrating the vinyl LP as Art, Amusement and Artifact." E-mail for subscription info.

THE WFMU CATALOG OF CURIOSITIES
P.O. Box 1568
Montclair, NJ 07042
phone (201) 678-4277
fax (201) 414-9225
http://wfmu.org

This free publication from the hallmark lounge radio station features CDs, books, videos, comics and, as the cover states, "stuff you need." The wacky ephemera ranges from the latest exotica CD reissues to kits for building your own theremin.

CHEESE BALL
510 Commonwealth Ave. #123
Boston, MA 02215
(617) 433-7069

editor Stacey Elizabeth Toon

Monthly 'zine in New England with retro feel that includes lounge news and features. Goes by this motto: "If it's good enough for grandpa, it's good enough for me!"

LOUNGE

315 S. Willaman Drive, Bungalow #1

Los Angeles, CA 90048

(310) 859-8665

lounge@netcom.com

Excellent newsprint magazine purporting to be "the guide to post-war culture." Publishes six times annually with great news, features and guides to lounge music and culture, all with great design and support (note the many record company ads). Writing always sparkles, and the departments are lively and enlightening, particularly the Dive Bar of the Month.

VERY VICKY

P.O. Box 383286

Cambridge, MA 02238

This lounge-themed comic book features fashion tips and lounge recommendations in addition to the harrowing graphic tales of Vicky Ocean, the world's most fab female, doing battle with blues singers and demonic Shriners. All without a single mascara run or a missed happy hour.

THE CONTINENTAL

P.O. Box 4336

Bellingham, WA 98227-4336

sberry@az.com

http://marie.az.com/~sberry/

This 'zine in the Northwest had evolved from garage-rock beginnings to embrace a good deal of lounge and exotica coverage. Lots of features and reviews.

CANNOT BECOME OBSOLETE

P.O. Box 1232

Lorton, VA 22199-1232

editor Vern Stoltz

What this 'zine lacks in print quality, it makes up for in sincere dedication to exotica and fringe lounge. Bills itself as "the zine that savors almost forgotten music."

DON'T BRUISE THE GIN

c/o Marc A

2210 Parklake Drive NE #100

Atlanta, GA 30345 - 2811

An occasional 'zine for the South's hot, swingin' lounge scene. Interviews, reviews and informational columns.

RE/SEARCH

Incredibly Strange Music, Vols. 1 and 2

edited by V. Vale & Andrea Juno

Newsweek referred to these two testaments as "the bible of lounge." These specialty publications (Nos. 14 and 15, respectively) are sometimes difficult to pin down now a couple of years later – and expect to drop just under $20 for each – but they are worth it for the serious lounge lizard. The real fringes of lounge and exotica are chronicled with great detail and loving care in interviews with collectors and artists (from the Cramps and Ken Nordine to Martin Denny and Esquivel). Each issue has a companion CD.

Note: V/Search Publications and Juno Books, the parent companies of the RE/Search line, now offer a new line of publications called XRE/Specs, including a recent title all about the swing revival. Read about them at http://www.postfun.com/xre/welcome.html.

DISCOVERIES MAGAZINE

922 Churchill St., Suite 1

Waupaca, WI 54981

phone (715) 258-7525

fax (715) 258-8707

jmkoenig@add-inc.com

http://www.csmonline.com/discoveries/

GOLDMINE MAGAZINE

700 E. State St.

Iola, WI 54990-0001

phone (715) 445-2214

fax (715) 445-4087

JeffTamar@aol.com

The rivalry between Goldmine and Discoveries has more to do with the fact that they're based in the same area code. For collectors, though, the history is irrelevant. Lounge and exotica hounds will find more satisfaction in the editorial copy and ads within Discoveries. Goldmine aims for a younger, more rock-oriented market, though it certainly does not ignore the lounge realm. When combing through the tedious dealer ads, hit both magazines, but start with Discoveries if you're pressed for time.

ORGAN AND BONGOS

P.O. Box 20396

Seattle, WA 98102

"A periodical guide to today's cocktail culture" that balances its cheeky attitude with design panache and the occasional great essay or feature story. Always fun to flip through, especially for the fake ads.

stations

National

KING KINI'S RADIO VELVET

An hour-long program from the swingers behind Minneapolis' Club Velvet. Playlists include such luminaries as Martin Denny, Esquivel, Ray Conniff and so on. Catch it coast to coast Sundays at midnight EST/9 p.m. PST on the following stations:

WPWA 1590-AM in Philadelphia

KPLS 830-AM in Los Angeles

WAUR 930-AM in Chicago

KIDR 740-AM in Phoenix

KKYD 1340-AM in Denver

KCAZ 1480-AM in Kansas City

KAHZ 1360-AM in Dallas-Ft. Worth

WWTC 1280-AM in Minneapolis-St. Paul

California

KCRW 89.9-FM LOS ANGELES

Stay Awake

Tuesdays and Thursdays midnight to 3 a.m.

A late-night show, hosted by Warren Kolodny, with a decided bend toward the lounge revival. Past shows have featured some intense lounge-music affi-ciandos.

KXLU 88.9-FM LOS ANGELES

Molotov Cocktail Hour

Tuesdays 11 p.m. to midnight

So Cal mobile DJ Senor Amor has been mixing up the sounds of the '50s and '60s here for six years. Expect a heady brew of rhumba, mambo, exotica, space-age pop and basic lounge fare peppered with a little surf and '50s garage creations.

Surfwave

Thursdays 11 p.m. to midnight

Jim Dunfrund's show is geared toward the surf set; however, what's surf culture without a little island mystery and post-hanging-10 imbibing? Offerings from the likes of Martin Denny or Don Ho keep things in check for the lounge crowd.

Stray Pop

Fridays midnight to 3 a.m.

This allegedly rock-oriented show is easily approached by the exotica crowd. The punkish hosts have entertained the likes of Korla Pandit before, and the show is seasoned with an exotic twist.

KABL 960-AM SAN FRANCISCO

A sure-fire fall-back plan when searching for some Sinatra or perhaps some Ray Conniff. The morning show features occasional interviews with lounge-savvy folks.

KFJC 89.7-FM SAN JOSE
House of Games
Sundays 9 a.m. - noon
Record dealer Jack Diamond's weekly pulpit is worth waking up for. Drawing from his immense stock, he spins hours of exotica and space-age pop, particularly Esquivel, before whom he must prostrate daily.

KCSB 91.9-FM SANTA BARBARA
High Fidelity
Mondays 8 to 10 p.m.
A good lounge show out of the Univ. of California-Sanata Barbara.

Illinois

WCBR 92.7-FM CHICAGO
Super Thriller Radio
Mondays 7 to 9 p.m.
A playlist that see-saws between old and new space-age sounds, from pop to ambient.

Kansas

KANZ 91.1-FM GARDEN CITY
KZNA 90.5-FM HILL CITY
The Mister Smooth Hour
Sundays 9 to 10 p.m.
The elusive Mr. Smooth usually starts each program with Dean Elliot's "You're the Top." From there, it's more easy-going lounge standards.

KANU 91.5-FM LAWRENCE
Retro Cocktail Hour
University of Kansas
Saturdays 7 to 8 p.m.
http://kuhttp.cc.ukans.edu/cwis/units/kanufm/retro.html
A plainly named lounge hour actually scheduled in prime time – in the Midwest! Good one, too, with your host Darrell Brogdon. Shows are usually themed toward a certain aspect of lounge music (i.e. a new compilation, percussionists, the islands, etc.).

Maine

WMPG 90.9-FM PORTLAND
My Vinyl Recliner
Tuesdays 10 to 11:30 p.m.
Typically a smooth coktail of lounge standards.

Massachusetts

WZBC 90.3-FM BOSTON
Music for Better Living
Wednesdays 6 to 7 p.m.
A healthy mix of exotica, Latin dance (especially mambo, samba, bossa nova and cha-cha), early Moog pop, crime jazz, pop vocals, space age pop and more. Hosted by two devoted collectors, Valerie and Peter.

WMBR 88.1-FM BOSTON
Three-Ring Circus
Fridays 4 to 6 p.m.
End your working week tuned to "Three-Ring Circus," an eclectic show with a lounge and surf leaning each Friday from 4 to 6 p.m. Old and new tunes mix for the modern-day lounge crowd. Then tune into "Jimmy's Easy" on Saturday nights for more lounge music.

Michigan

WXOU 88.3-FM AUBURN HILLS
Champagne and Dynamite
Thursdays 1 to 3 p.m.
Enlivening the station's normal programming, this afternoon set features standards from exotica and lounge, with the occasional dip into true jazz.

New Mexico

KRUX 91.5-FM LAS CRUCES
Expando Radio
Thursdays 10 p.m. to midnight
A hidden treasure in the desert, Michael Clifford's weekly show is a bizarre – often startling – blend of lounge music and recorded oddities.

websites

New York/New Jersey

WFMU, 91.1-FM/90.1-FM East Orange, NJ

The flagship station for the lounge revival. Check out "Trouble" from 9 a.m. to noon Tuesdays, billed as "sweet fuzz fro sounds from the ether," and the three-hour weekly show by "Ultra-Lounge" contributor Irwin Chusid (Wednesdays noon to 3 p.m.). This is the station keeping the flame in the tiki torch burning.

North Carolina

WQFS 90.9-FM Greensboro
Muzak for Dummies
Tuesdays 9 p.m. to midnight
http://listen.to/wqfs
Ultra-lush (be that an adjective of texture or sobriety) evening show that sends you to sleep – or at least into a blissful dream state – with fluid instrumentals, old and new. They used to give out free tapes if you e-mailed them.

Pennsylvania

WKPS 90.7-FM University Park
Jet-Set Sounds in Hi-Fi
Saturdays 11 a.m. to 1 p.m.
http://www.clubs.psu.edu/wkps/
Two hours out of Penn State featuring the basics of lounge and space-age pop plus a few crooners.

Texas

KOOP 91.7-FM Austin
The Lounge Show
Saturdays 10 a.m. to noon
A fairly mellow late-morning stretcher loaded with lounge and void of commercials.

The Mountain Biking Lounge Music Page
http://www.charged.com/dirt/stories/mnt_lounge/
This odd niche on the web brings lounge music squarely into the '90s by discussing its link to the mountain-biking sport community. You don't think lounge and mountain biking can relate aesthetically? Dial up this page for a defense of this bizarre union. Also, find out which lounge albums make the best listening for certain biking trails in California.

Frank and Carole's Lindy Hop Weekly
http://www.dalmatiancorporation.com/lindy/index.html
This older couple in D.C. travels around the country every chance they get, looking for places to show off their swing dancing. While their passion and their site is geared toward a different aesthetic than the lounge phenomenon, the overlapping tastes in clubs and ballrooms is noteworthy. They've charted a myriad of dancehalls, societies and clubs all over the country and listed their discoveries here in immense detail.

The Rat Pack
http://www.primenet.com/~drbmbay/
A site "dedicated – in part, and there's more, so much, much more – to those Groovy Entertainers, those Kings of Swings otherwise known as The Rat Pack!" Stop by and send your fellow swingers one of six available e-postcards featuring great Rat Pack photos.

The Exotica Mailing List
http://www.swcp.com/~lazlo/Lists/Exotica.html
This page explains how to subscribe to a mailing list covering exotica music. A complete archive of postings to the list is also available from this site, as are numerous other lounge links.

The Space Age Pop Standards Page
http://home.earthlink.net/~spaceagepop/index.htm

A site that approaches the music from an oft-ignored perspective: the songs'. With all the colorful personalities and liquor around these lounges of ours, we sometimes forget how great the original songs are – and how many times performers retooled them. Do you know many lounge artists covered, and even titled their albums, "Yellow Bird"? Keeping to its motto – "Any song worth playing is worth wearing into the ground" – this site explores the songs themselves, with lists of their reproduction by numerous artists. Also included here are priceless cross-listing and biographies of not only the performers but the conductors, arrangers and songwriters, plus a helpful overview of the music and a compilation of great liner notes.

LOUNGE LOS ANGELES
http://www.val.net/Lounge/

Comprehensive guide to the scene in the City of Angels, with essays, features, reviews, club listings, links and the Alco-Hall of Fame.

SWANK-O-RAMA
http://www.mindspring.com/~jpmckay/

This site, "dedicated to better living through cocktail culture," brings together various elements that make up the lounge ouevre – the music, the dance-steps, the drink recipes – in a well-rounded presentation. The introduction invites all to see the light, "whether you are a secret agent, a playboy, a 'La Dolce Vita' jet-setter , a super-model or just someone looking for an lifetime of fabulous fun," even emploring the masses to "cast off your flannel shirts and pour out your pitchers of beer!"

THE ROOTS OF LOUNGE
http://www.gonix.com/rol

These pages suffice as a survey course in the origins and devlopment of lounge music, from the dawn of the LP to the music's descent into novelty. The information comes from a public radio documentary.

COCKTAIL MAGAZINE
http://www.cocktail.com/

Loads of information about great bars around the country is featured here along with a chunk of drink recipes. A must for mixmasters.

NIGHTCLUB AND BAR MAGAZINE
http://www.nightclub.com/

Primarily a trade publication, this web site is of value to clubgoers for its drink lists (complete with a few professional tips) and its search engine for bars and clubs in every state – allegedly "the most comprehensive club/bar directory on the web."

THE FABULOUS BUD E. LUV
http://www.budeluv.com/

Bud E. Luv is a Boston-native entertainer transplanted to California as a kitschy lounge act. The site is worth seeing for more reasons than just finding out where the Budster is performing; it's loaded with amusing anecdotes, photos and interactive fun. You can play poker and blackjack in the casino, order a drink at the bar and request a song in the lounge. Also read about "Why Some Babes Go Nuts for the Budster" and "Some Musical Trends I've Created."

MATT HELM'S SWINGING WEB SITE
http://members.aol.com/matthelm2/matthelm.htm

A fairly comprehensive fan site featuring discussions of films, music and people and including an evolving list of clubs and lounges around the country and Canada.

SPACE SAFARI
"To Hi-Fidelity and Beyond!"
http://easyweb.easynet.co.uk/~rcb/space/

Run by an Edinburgh DJ, this site has all the information and reviews you need for a quest into the spacey frontiers of exotica music – or, as he calls it, "off-world lounge music."

THE WILDS SCENE
http://www.wildsscene.com/

This delicious exotica site has it all. There are music pointers and moments of grand celebration, like the collection of Liner Notes of the Gods, and there are wacky galleries of tiki and lounge ephemera – even a viewing of items carved from coconuts.

VIK TROLA'S LOUNGE OF SELF-INDULGENCE
http://www.chaoskitty.com/sabpm/

A lounge staple site since 1995, this site include's the cyber-swank Vik's Lounge, Radio Vik (using Real Audio) and the popular Space Age Bachelor Pad Music site. The last fist full of pages includes a gallery of exotica album covers, a wealth of details about Esquivel's recorded output and numerous pointers for where to find lounge music. In fact, the details in the listings for radio programs, record shops and 'zines surpass even our humble efforts here.

ELECTROTONE
http://www.electrotone.com/

Possibly the best web design we've seen in lounge pages, Electrotone is a swank online 'zine with reviews, culture and a dead-on definition of the lounge ouevre.

THE COCKTAIL PARTY
http://www.cocktailparty.com/

An esoteric site devoted to the simple joys of enjoying refreshing drinks at home. Learn a little bartending lingo, too.

BACHELOR PAD ONLINE
http://userpages.itis.com/xjasong/

Not much to recommend this site, except that it does feature a chat room for non-linear discussions of lounge music and culture.

ULTRA-LOUNGE
http://www.ultralounge.com/Volumes/links.html

The web page for Capitol's multi-volume "Ultra-Lounge" series of compilation CDs features music information and great links.

THE MUSICOLOGY POD
http://www.tripod.com/pod_central/pods/musicology/

This is a clearinghouse for serious music discussion. This centralized site features some articles and a weekly chat session, but it also provides links to nearly 3,000 personal music discussion sites, including several related to lounge and exotica.

COCKTAIL
http://www.hotwired.com/cocktail/

A brainy discussion of the pleasures of imbibing, including frequent use of the word "mixologist" and mentions of certain cocktails' pedigrees. The place to cram for serious bartending brainiacs. Don't miss the carefully researched Drink of the Week, but – as the San Francisco Bay Guardian advised – "just as you wouldn't stage-dive at a Combustible Edison show, don't look for a recipe for Sex on the Beach in Cocktail."

notes

acknowledgements

FOREVER LOUNGE *would* swing far less without *John Koenig, Gary Johnson and Tony Lillis. Kudos, to boot, to Mike Keller, Deb and Lori, Tom Rush, Artie Decco at Borders in Seattle, web masters Otto von Stroheim, Vik Trola and Brad Bigelow, Bill and Cindy at C-Bub, Andre Hinds, Ira Robbins, Jerry Osborne, Elliot Kendall and Bryan Thomas at Del-Fi, all at the All-Music Guide, Spud and Conky, James Vance, Michael H. Price, Larry King, Rita Sherrow, Dennis King, Jim Watts, Cathy Logan, Steve Ramm, Cary Mansfield, Kelly, Daniel, 'Martini' Lou, Bret & Cynthia and Ken & Bonna.* Long live Sammy!

about the authors

John Wooley *is an author, journalist and scriptwriter who lives exactly 1.2 miles from the world's largest totem pole.*

Thomas Conner *is an obsessed, self-medicated pop music critic living in Tulsa, Oklahoma.*

Mark Brown *is a newspaper-man with a casual fascination of English pop culture, strong coffee, and his wife's piano playing.*

Mike Keller

When they're not lounging, the authors work in the Tulsa World entertainment department.

(photographed at Camerelli's, Tulsa, Oklahoma)